Professional Pilot's Study Guide
Volume 9

Undercarriages

Professional Pilot's Study Guide Volume 9

Undercarriages

Mike Burton

Airlife
England

Copyright © 1993 Mike Burton

First published in the UK in 1993
by Airlife Publishing Ltd

British Library Cataloguing in Publication Data
A catalogue record of this book is available from the British Library

ISBN 1 85310 281 4

Printed in England by Livesey Ltd, Shrewsbury SY3 9EB

Airlife Publishing Ltd

101 Longden Road, Shrewsbury SY3 9EB

Contents

Section 1   The Undercarriage Unit   1

Introduction **1**   Purpose **1**   Retractable Undercarriage Units **2**
Fixed Undercarriage Unit **3**   Shock Absorber **3**   Wheel Assemblies **4**
Undercarriage Position Indication **5**   Basic Undercarriage Operation
During Retraction **5**   Undercarriage Emergency Operation **6**

Section 2   Undercarriage Layouts   9

Introduction **9**   Tricycle Undercarriage Layout **9**   Advantages and
Disadvantages of Nose Wheel Layouts **10**   Advantages and
Disadvantages of Tail Wheel Layouts **10**   Tandem Undercarriage
Layout **11**   Advantages and Disadvantages of Tandem Undercarriage
Layout **11**   Multi-undercarriage and Multi-wheel Layouts **12**   The
Number of Wheels Employed **13**   Bogie Trim **14**   Bogie Trail **14**
Castoring or Cross-Wind Landing Gear **15**

Section 3   Brake Units   17

Introduction **17**   Drum Brakes **17**   The Plate Brake **17**   Plate Type Brake
Unit (Piston Rod Adjustment Type) **18**   The Torque Plate **19**   The
Operating Cylinders or Actuators **19**   Emergency Brake Operation **21**
Brake Plates **21**   Friction Pads **22**   The Caliper Type Brake Unit **22**   The
Multi-Segmented Plate Type Brake Unit **23**   Torque Plate **24**   Thrust
Ring **24**   The Operating Cylinders or Actuators **24**   Automatic Brake
Adjuster Operation **25**   The Rotor Assemblies **25**   The Stator
Assemblies **26**   The Wear Indicators **26**

Section 4   Aircraft Wheels   30

Introduction **30**   Basic Construction **30**   Tubeless Tyre Wheel
Assembly **32**   Wheel Bearings **33**   Fusible Alloy Plugs **33**

Section 5   Aircraft Tyres   37

Introduction **37**   The Function of the Tyre **37**   Tubed Tyre Construction **37**
Component Parts of a Tubed Tyre **38**   Tubeless Tyre Construction **39**
Advantages of a Tubeless Tyre **39**   Regions of a Tyre **40**   Tyre Treads **40**
Specialist Tyre Treads **41**   Tyre Markings **42**   Tyre Size Markings **42**
The Tyre Part Number **43**   Serial Number **43**   Ply Rating **43**   Speed
Rating **43**   Other Markings **44**   High Pressure Tyres **44**   Tyre Creep **44**
Tyre Creep Marks **44**   Tyre Wear **45**   Tyre Pressures **46**   Conducting
Tyres **47**

Section 6   Wheel Brake Operating System   50

Introduction **50**   Basic Wheel Brake Hydraulic System **50**   The Brake
Accumulator **51**   Operation of the Brake Control Valve **51**   Brake
Operation **52**   Anti-Skid Unit **52**

Section 7   Brake Unit Anti-Skid Systems   54

Introduction **54**   Purpose **54**   Mechanical Anti-Skid System **54**
Mechanical Anti-Skid System Operation **55**   Installation of
Mechanical Anti-Skid Unit **55**   Electronic Anti-Skid Unit **56**

Section 8   Shock Absorbers   59

Introduction **59**   Shock Absorber Types **59**   Oleo Pneumatic Shock Absorber (without Separator) **59**   Oleo Pneumatic Shock Absorber (with Separator) **60**   Oil Compression Strut **61**   Load/Extension Graph **61**   Extension of Shock Absorber Measurement **63**

Section 9   Summary of Pre-Flight Checks   66

Introduction **66**   The General Structure **66**   Tyre Inspection **68**   Wheel Inspection **68**   Shock Absorbers **69**   Heat and Stress Paint **69**   Brake Units **69**   Anti-Skid Units **69**

Final Practice Questions   71

1

THE UNDERCARRIAGE UNIT

1.1 Introduction

The term undercarriage, or alighting gear, is a term used to describe the assemblies attached to the underside of the aircraft upon which the aircraft alights, taxies and stands upon when parked on the ground, sometimes for long periods. For the purpose of this explanation it will be assumed that it is a land-based aircraft and is equipped with a wheeled undercarriage.

1.2 Purpose

When landing, the undercarriage is required to absorb the impact of the landing at touch-down by means of the following:

(a) A shock absorber to absorb compression loads.

(b) A drag strut to absorb drag loads.

(c) A side load strut to absorb side loads.

A typical undercarriage unit is shown in Fig.1-1.

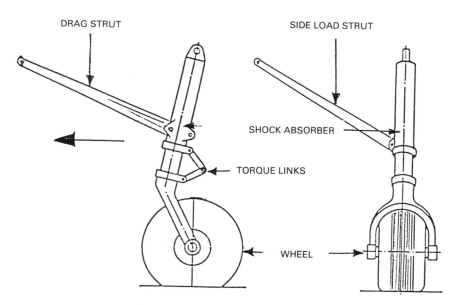

Fig.1-1. Basic Undercarriage Unit.

1.3   Retractable Undercarriage Units

In order to reduce drag when the aircraft is in normal flight most undercarriages are retractable which is normally achieved by hydraulic actuation.

Most main undercarriages are retracted sideways into the wing or the bottom of the fuselage adjacent to the wing root. Some high winged aircraft retract their undercarriages into special fairings at the base of the fuselage.

The nose undercarriage unit is normally retracted forwards or backwards into a compartment near the nose of the aircraft. Where space in the nose, or front fuselage area of the fuselage is a problem, the undercarriage may be retracted sideways. Fig.1-2 shows a number of examples of retraction.

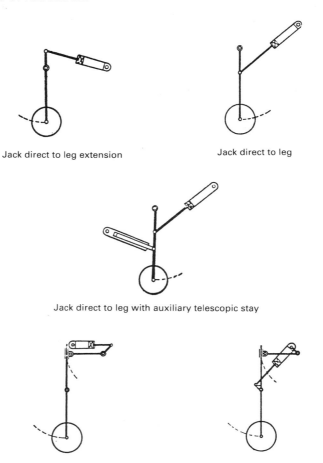

Jack direct to leg extension

Jack direct to leg

Jack direct to leg with auxiliary telescopic stay

Hinged link slides on leg,
jack on link

Hinged link slides on leg,
jack between link and leg

Fig.1-2. Configuration of Retraction Systems.

2

1.4   Fixed Undercarriage Unit

Some undercarriage units, particular on light aircraft, may be non-retractable or fixed. An example is shown in Fig.1-3.

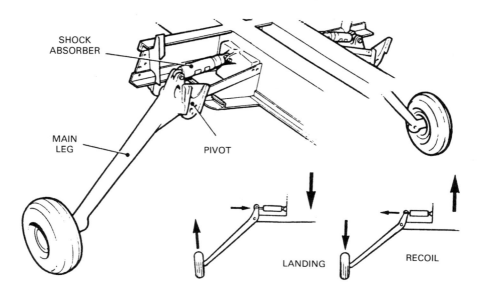

Fig.1-3. Fixed Undercarriage with Shock Absorbers.

The undercarriage must be attached to strong points of the aircraft which are capable of withstanding the considerable impact loads experienced when landing; to this end the main undercarriage units are usually attached directly or indirectly to the main spar.

The nose undercarriage is normally attached to strengthened frames adjacent to the nose of the aircraft. A similar method is employed on tail wheeled aircraft in that a strengthened area of the rear fuselage is used.

1.5   Shock Absorber

The shock absorber has two primary functions, the first to absorb the compression loads imposed by the impact of landing and the second to dampen the tendency to recoil, that is to say the shock absorbers tendency to rapidly extend again immediately after absorbing the landing impact.

The shock absorber must also be designed to withstand considerable bending loads which it will also experience when landing, taxying and in particular when the aircraft is being turned when on the ground.

The shock absorber consists primarily of two cylinders which slide one inside the other much like a telescope. To prevent one cylinder rotating inside the other, torque links or toggles are used.

Fig.1-4 shows an example of a set of Torque Links or Toggles as used on a shock absorber unit.

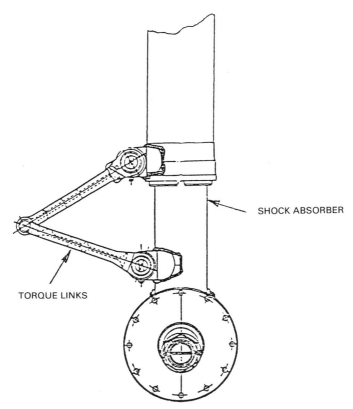

SHOCK ABSORBER

TORQUE LINKS

Fig. 1-4. Undercarriage Torque Links or Toggles.

On some lighter types of aircraft the inner cylinder of the shock absorber is prevented from rotating within the outer cylinder by splines on the cylinders.

1.6 Wheel Assemblies

The wheel assembly consists of a wheel and tyre and usually housed within the main undercarriage wheels is the brake unit. The number of wheels employed on a particular aircraft is dictated by the physical wheel loading and the type of runway to be used. It is the function of the wheel and tyre assemblies to spread the load of the aircraft over a given area to produce an individual wheel loading that is acceptable within the strength limits of the runway. Hence large heavy aircraft tend to have a greater number of wheel assemblies. The tyre size and shape is also important in this function in that a large balloon type of tyre will again spread the load over a greater area. At the same time consideration must be made to the space available for stowage of the undercarriage units and as a result often a compromise must be reached in design. This in some cases has led to complex undercarriage trim systems in which, in simple terms, the assembly is physically folded prior to retraction. Such systems will be discussed in more detail later.

1.7   Undercarriage Position Indication

The most common form of undercarriage position indicator is a system of lights. Undercarriage down and locked down is shown by a green light, or lights, normally one light for each undercarriage unit being used. On a three undercarriage arrangement three green lights will be illuminated, one for the nose or tail undercarriage, and one for each main undercarriage.

When the undercarriage is in motion and/or unlocked, the green lights are replaced with the illumination of red lights. When the undercarriage is fully up and locked up all lights are extinguished.

Down   — Locked down   — Green
Unlocked   — or in motion   — Red
Up   — Locked up   — All lights out

Fig.1-5 shows an example undercarriage position indicator.

On some aircraft undercarriage position lights are replaced by magnetic indicators.

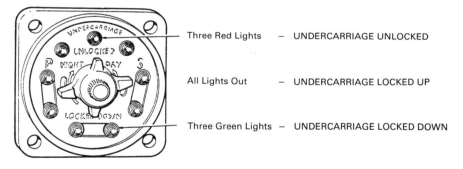

Three Red Lights   — UNDERCARRIAGE UNLOCKED

All Lights Out   — UNDERCARRIAGE LOCKED UP

Three Green Lights — UNDERCARRIAGE LOCKED DOWN

Fig.1-5. Undercarriage Position Indicator.

1.8   Basic Undercarriage Operation During Retraction

Most modern undercarriages are retracted by hydraulic actuation, a small number of older types use pneumatics (compressed air) to achieve this function. In most cases when the undercarriage is selected up the sequence followed is as follows:

(a) On selection of undercarriage up the undercarriage door opens.

(b) Undercarriage down locks are withdrawn.

(c) Undercarriage position lights change from green to red.

(d) Undercarriage retracts.

(e) Undercarriage uplocks engage, door closes, door locks engage and lights change from red to extinguished.

The reverse takes place when the undercarriage is selected down. On most undercarriage systems the undercarriage doors close again after the undercarriage has extended to reduce aerodynamic drag, important at take off, and to reduce foreign objects being thrown up into the undercarriage bays when the aircraft is in motion, by the aircraft wheels.

1.9 Undercarriage Emergency Operation.

In the event of hydraulic system failure the undercarriage may be lowered in an emergency by either a back up, or standby, hydraulic system or more commonly by the use of compressed air which is stored in cylinders in the aircraft for such a purpose.

Selection for emergency lowering of the undercarriage is normally by a separate emergency selector.

TEST YOURSELF 1
THE UNDERCARRIAGE UNIT

1. The inner cylinder of the shock absorber is prevented from rotating inside the outer cylinder by:
   (a) torque links.
   (b) hydraulic dampers.
   (c) twist links.
   (d) compression links.

   Ref. 1.5.

2. When a retractable undercarriage is down and locked down the undercarriage position indicator lights will indicate:
   (a) all lights out.
   (b) three red lights.
   (c) three green lights.
   (d) three 'D's.

   Ref. 1.7.

3. A red undercarriage position indicator light indicates:
   (a) undercarriage failure.
   (b) the undercarriage is locked down.
   (c) the undercarriage is up and locked up.
   (d) the undercarriage is unlocked.

   Ref. 1.7.

4. Undercarriage trim is a term used to describe:
   (a) the positioning of the undercarriage prior to landing.
   (b) the positioning of the undercarriage to keep the aircraft straight on the runway.
   (c) the rotation of the nose undercarriage for steering purposes.
   (d) the folding of the undercarriage prior to retraction.

   Ref. 1.6.

5. Large 'Balloon' tyres are used on some types of aircraft to:
   (a) reduce undercarriage weight.
   (b) reduce aerodynamic drag.
   (c) spread the aircraft weight over a greater area.
   (d) increase the aircraft wheel loading.

   Ref. 1.6.

6. The wheel brake units are normally housed:
   (a) adjacent to the wheel units.
   (b) within the wheel units of both main and nose undercarriages.
   (c) within the main undercarriage wheel units.
   (d) within the nose or tail undercarriage units.

   Ref. 1.6.

7. Undercarriage units are normally attached to:
   (a) the leading edge of the underside of the wing.
   (b) the main spar where possible.
   (c) the trailing edge of the wing.
   (d) the fuselage only.

   Ref. 1.4.

8. The nose undercarriage unit is normally retracted:
   (a) forward into the fuselage.
   (b) rearward into the fuselage.
   (c) forward, rearward or sideways into the fuselage.
   (d) rearwards into the fuselage to reduce aerodynamic drag.

   Ref. 1.3.

9. During landing, drag loads on the undercarriage are absorbed by:
   (a) drag struts.
   (b) torque links.
   (c) the shock absorber only.
   (d) a hydraulic damper.

   Ref. 1.2.

10 On an undercarriage position indicator, in flight, all lights out indicates:
   (a) power failure.
   (b) the undercarriage is in motion.
   (c) the undercarriage is locked down.
   (d) the undercarriage is locked up.

   Ref. 1.7.

2

UNDERCARRIAGE LAYOUTS

2.1 Introduction

The majority of undercarriage layouts take the form of the conventional tricycle undercarriage. This comprises two main undercarriage assemblies, one under each wing, and a nose or tail wheel undercarriage unit. In some undercarriage designs the tricycle design has not been used due to specialist aircraft design requirements. One such alternative arrangement that may be adopted is the tandem, or bicycle under-carriage in which design the main undercarriage units are arranged one behind the other mounted under the fuselage. This usually requires some form of outrigger to be placed under each wing to provide additional stability.

Variations of some alternative designs are discussed in this chapter.

2.2 Tricycle Undercarriage Layout

The tricycle undercarriage is the most widely used layout on modern civil aircraft. Fig.2-1 shows a classical example of a tricycle undercarriage comprising two main units and one nose unit.

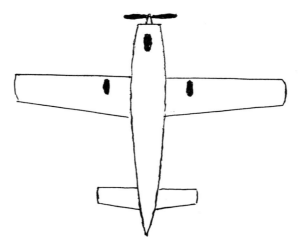

Fig.2-1. Tricycle Undercarriage.

Whilst most modern aircraft employ a nose undercarriage, some employ a tail wheel instead. This has a few advantages but many disadvantages. The tail wheel layout will be discussed later.

2.3   Advantages and Disadvantages of Nose Wheel Layouts

(a) Advantages

(1) Heavy braking cannot cause nosing over or overturning.

(2) The aircraft when landing, particularly in a cross-wind, or with a drift, is inherently stable, as the c.g. is ahead of the main wheels.

(3) At touch down the aircraft pitches forward, spoiling the wing lift and eliminating any risk of aerodynamic bounce.

(4) The pilot's visibility is a maximum at all times.

(5) The floor line of the aircraft is always more or less horizontal, which is an advantage for freight loading or to the passengers.

(6) There is no loss of take-off performance due to drag from a tail-down attitude during initial acceleration.

(7) The short wheelbase facilitates manoeuvring, particularly with power steering.

(b) Disadvantages

(1) A nose wheel will be heavier than a tail wheel for an equivalent airframe, due to the short wheelbase, and also due to the forward pitching of the aircraft during braking which increases the dynamic loads on the nose wheel.

(2) Retraction of a nose wheel is often awkward, particularly if the nose of the aircraft is provided with a radar scanner, or an air duct to the engine.

(3) Very little of the forward energy of the aircraft is dissipated by air drag; the brakes must thus be able to deal with most of it.

(4) Heavy braking causes a reduction of main wheel loading, tending to cause wheel skidding, and making more desirable automatic brake anti-skid devices.

Notwithstanding these disadvantages the nose wheel layout is the most widely adopted, and indeed can be considered as virtually standardised.

2.4   Advantages and Disadvantages of Tail Wheel Layouts

(a) Advantages

(1) A minimum auxiliary wheel weight when disposed well at the rear of the aircraft.

(2) Location of the auxiliary wheel in a relatively unimportant part of the fuselage.

(3) Dissipation of some (perhaps 25 per cent) of the total forward energy in air drag due to the tail-down attitude when landing, energy which would otherwise have to be absorbed by the brakes.

(4) The location of the main, braked wheels in front of the centre of gravity of the aircraft means that the wheel loading is increased when the brakes are applied. This tends to prevent troubles due to locking of the wheels and means that automatic skid detecting devices are not needed to reduce tyre wear.

(b) Disadvantages

(1) Heavy braking can cause nosing over or overturning of the aircraft, and the degree of braking permitted must be restricted to safe values.

(2) Brake drag forces, being applied forward of the c.g., cause a tendency for the aircraft to swing round. This can only be prevented by rudder action (ineffective at low speed), differential braking, or use of a tail wheel lock. The degree of skill required by a pilot, particularly at night, is considerable when brakes are applied heavily; the swing-factor is perhaps the main criticism of the tail wheel layout.

(3) On touch down the aircraft tail drops; this increases incidence causing a tendency for aerodynamic bouncing or ballooning.

(4) The pilot's visibility is poor during taxying.

(5) The loading of the aircraft with freight and passengers is complicated by the inclined floor line.

(6) Take-off is made more difficult by the increased drag until the tail can be raised.

Fig.2-2 shows an example of a Tail Wheeled Undercarriage Layout.

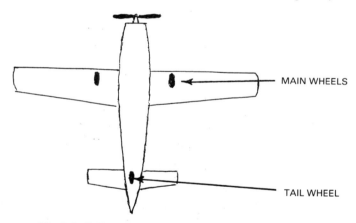

MAIN WHEELS

TAIL WHEEL

Fig.2-2. Tail Wheeled Undercarriage Layout.

2.5 Tandem Undercarriage Layout

This type of arrangement may also be termed a Bicycle Type Undercarriage.

In general this type of arrangement has been deemed unsuitable for most civil aircraft applications. Generally it has few advantages over the tricycle arrangement.

2.6 Advantages and Disadvantages of Tandem Undercarriage Layout

(a) Advantages

(1) Elimination of large wheels and legs from the wings.

(2) Good fore and aft stability.

(b) Disadvantages

    (1) Higher weight (the overall penalty being at least 0.75 per cent of the aircraft weight) due to the weight of the auxiliary outriggers arising from the substantial dynamic loads they must bear when landing one wing down.

    (2) Take-off incidence is difficult to obtain, as the speed at 'unstick' is high.

    (3) Landing is more difficult than with a normal aircraft because the correct attitude must be achieved. It is not possible to run along on the rear wheels alone (as on a tricycle), and landing front wheel first tends to cause ballooning off.

    (4) Automatic braking devices are essential because of the wide variation in loads on the main wheels.

    (5) Both the front wheel and the outriggers must be castoring. There are thus three legs to be designed with centring and anti-shimmy devices.

Fig.2-3 shows an example of a Tandem Undercarriage Layout.

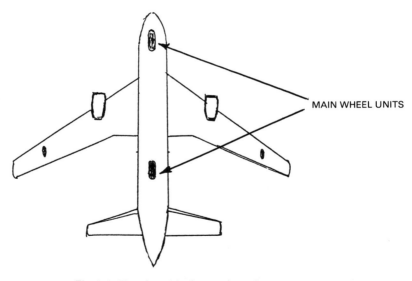

MAIN WHEEL UNITS

Fig.2-3. Tandem Undercarriage Layout.

2.7 Multi-Undercarriage and Multi-wheel Layouts

Most four or more wheel layouts will have the wheels arranged symmetrically about, and not far from, the aircraft centre line. Some modern aircraft have been, however, produced with four main legs, in an attempt to spread the load of the aircraft more evenly into the wing. As pure vertical loading is often not the main condition to be dealt with, this arrangement may not be satisfactory in practice; it may be penalised under side or manoeuvring loads.

A typical multi-wheel layout is shown in Fig.2-4.

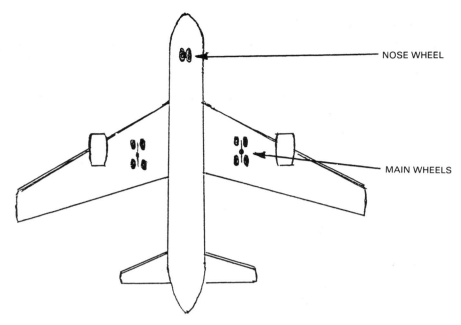

NOSE WHEEL

MAIN WHEELS

Fig.2-4. Multi-Wheel Main Undercarriage Layout.

Where runways exist that are capable of taking only comparatively light loads, multi-wheel, or 'Bogie' undercarriage units have to be employed to spread the aircraft load over a greater area, thereby reducing the wheel loading, thus allowing large aircraft to use relatively small airports.

2.8   The Number of Wheels Employed

On each undercarriage leg the number of wheels may vary considerably and is normally dictated by the individual wheel loading required, in order to achieve flexible operations, and the space available in the wings, or fuselage, into which the undercarriage may be retracted.

Fig.2-5 shows some variations on multi-wheel undercarriage units.

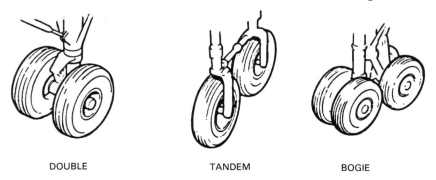

DOUBLE   TANDEM   BOGIE

Fig.2-5. Some Multi-Wheeled Units.

13

2.9 Bogie Trim

Because of the complexity of 'Bogie', or multi-wheel unit design it is necessary to fold, or trim the undercarriage unit prior to its physical retraction into the undercarriage bay in order it will take up less space. If trim is not carried out on some undercarriage types this may lead to the requirement of thicker wing sections and/or less space available for fuel storage or other equipments.

An example of an undercarriage in its normal and trimmed condition is shown in Fig.2-6.

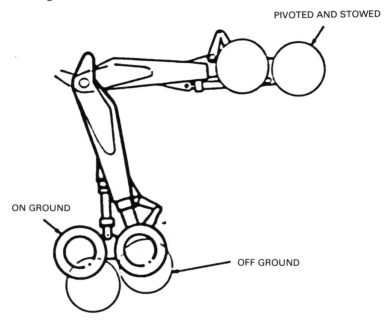

Fig.2-6. Bogie Trim.

The trimming action of the undercarriage is an automatic function which is completed during the retraction sequence by a series of hydraulic sequence valves and hydraulic jacks. When undercarriage up is selected the trim sequence is automatically set in motion and does not require any separate selection on the part of the pilot.

2.10 Bogie Trail

Most bogie undercarriage units are designed to trail rear wheels down on landing. The purpose of this trail is to allow the 'Spin Up' of the wheels on landing to be progressive and therefore reduce the torque reaction generated on the assembly to one pair of wheels at a time thereby reducing the slamming effect of the nose wheel onto the runway. This may be assisted by the fitting of small shock absorbers to the bogie assembly as shown on Fig.2-7. These shock absorbers are sometimes called 'Hop Dampers' or 'Dash Pots'.

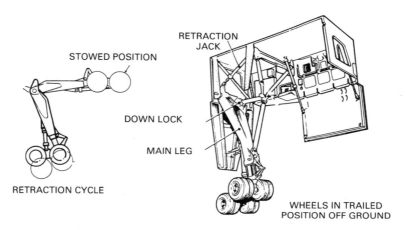

Fig.2-7. Bogie Undercarriage Unit with Trail.

2.11 Castoring or Cross-wind Landing Gear

The auxiliary wheel of a tail wheel or nose wheel layout will normally be castoring to enable the aircraft to manoeuvre about the main wheels. Aircraft have been produced with all three wheels castoring, the so-called cross-wind landing gear system.

Fig.2-8 shows an aircraft fitted with castoring main wheels. It is of interest to note the original Bleriot monoplane that flew the Channel in 1909 was fitted with castoring landing gear. Then, as now, the main purpose was to enable the aircraft to take-off and land in a cross-wind; a normal tyre will slip a few degrees sideways without creating excess side load, but a yaw of more than about five degrees imposes serious side loads on the landing with the fixed and castoring landing gear. Fig.2-8 shows the two conditions which arise at take-off and landing with the fixed and castoring landing gears. The normal landing technique with an orthodox aircraft is for the pilot when landing yawed in a cross-wind to align the aircraft up to the runway at the last moment before touch down to avoid serious side scrubbing loads on the wheels and indeed the risk of a severe swing. The castoring system enables the wheels to follow the true direction of motion, notwithstanding that the aircraft may be 'vectored' into the wind.

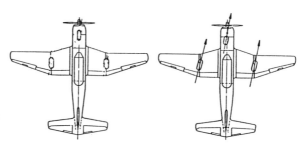

Fig.2-8. Castoring or Cross-wind Landing Gear.

TEST YOURSELF 2
UNDERCARRIAGE LAYOUTS

1. On a nose-wheeled tricycle undercarriage system:
   (a) dynamic loads on the nose undercarriage will be reduced during braking.
   (b) retraction of a nose undercarriage is easier than with a tail undercarriage.
   (c) greater dynamic loads will be experienced when braking.
   (d) heavy braking will tend to increase loading on the main undercarriage units.

   Ref. 2.2.

2. Dissipation of the total forward energy of the aircraft during landing of a tail wheeled aircraft may be:
   (a) as much as 25 per cent aerodynamic braking.
   (b) as much as 50 per cent aerodynamic braking.
   (c) as little as 15 per cent aerodynamic braking.
   (d) as little as 5 per cent aerodynamic braking.

   Ref. 2.4.

3. On a nose wheeled aircraft:
   (a) most of the braking is aerodynamic.
   (b) wheel brakes have to be more efficient than with a tail wheel undercarriage type.
   (c) braking efficiency has to be approximately equal to a tail wheel type.
   (d) heavy wheel braking is less stable than with a tail wheel unit.

   Ref. 2.3.

4. A nose wheeled aircraft on landing will produce:
   (a) poorer visibility of the ground.
   (b) less air drag than a tail wheeled aircraft.
   (c) a reduced wheel loading on the nose wheel.
   (d) an increase of main wheel loading during braking.

   Ref. 2.3.

5. A tandem undercarriage permits:
   (a) thinner wings to be employed.
   (b) a shorter take-off run.
   (c) larger wheels to be employed.
   (d) the elimination of anti-skid devices.

   Ref. 2.6.

3

BRAKE UNITS

3.1 Introduction

The brake unit is attached to the undercarriage leg adjacent to the axle on which the wheel is mounted. When fully assembled the brake unit is located within the wheel, so as the wheel rotates it also rotates the brake drum or brake disc. When brakes are applied friction is generated converting the forward motion of the aircraft into heat energy, thereby retarding, or slowing down the aircraft. The brakes may be operated by air (Pneumatic Brakes) or by hydraulic fluid (Hydraulic Brakes) which forces a friction shoe or pad against the drum or disc.

The brakes are controlled from the cockpit and on selection may provide progressive braking which is achieved by a careful increase of brake pressure and so progressively slows the aircraft. Differential braking is also provided on many aircraft to provide a means of steering the aircraft by selection of one brake or the other. Port brake to turn the aircraft to port and starboard brake selected to turn the aircraft to starboard.

A brief description is given here of the basic types of brake unit and their operation.

3.2 Drum Brakes

This type of brake unit is used in the main on older types of aircraft. Fig.3-1 shows an example of a simple drum brake. The drum is attached to the wheel and rotates with the wheel and tyre assembly. The brake unit is attached to the undercarriage unit at the wheel axle attachment point and remains stationary. The type illustrated is operated by compressed air which is supplied by the aircraft pneumatic system.

When brakes are applied air enters the brake bag; this is a form of flattened tube, which is caused to expand, forcing the brake blocks, or shoes against the drum thus generating friction. As the bag expands it does so against the action of a series of return springs which, when brakes are released, returns the brake blocks or shoes to their original position. This type of brake unit is prone to brake fade, which is the reduction of braking force due to the expansion of the drum as a result of heat.

3.3 The Plate Brake

With the introduction of heavier aircraft into service, higher landing speeds and, on most aircraft, the adoption of nose wheeled tricycle undercarriages which reduces aerodynamic braking leaves more kinetic energy to be absorbed by the wheel brakes, to be converted to heat. The

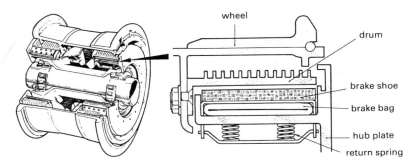

Fig.3-1. Drum Brake Unit.

drum brake design could not cope with such high loads and so the disc or plate brake was developed. This brake dispenses with the drum and operates by the gripping action of non-rotating friction pads against a disc, or plate, keyed to rotate with the wheel.

The development of the plate brake has passed through two primary phases. The early type which used chromium plated copper plates and organic friction pad material followed by the introduction of plates or discs which are made of steel used with inorganic friction pad material.

The latter type which uses steel plates, usually termed rotors and, inorganic friction pads, usually termed stators is the most common type in use today.

It must be noted there are many variations of these brake units in use and so a general type is used in this chapter to show how each primary design is constructed and how it operates.

Although all plate brakes operate on the same principle there are three basic designs which are:

(a) The piston rod adjustment type.

(b) The caliper type.

(c) Segmented plate type, also known as a 'Heat Pack'.

3.4 Plate Type Brake Unit (Piston Rod Adjustment Type)

Many older types of aircraft in use still use this type of brake unit design and it is included in this chapter to show the general stages of development and to give a good understanding of the wheel brakes to pilots that may fly such equipped aircraft types.

The piston rod adjustment type brake unit consists of the following basic parts:

(a) The torque plate.

(b) The friction pads.

(c) The operating cylinders or actuators.

(d) The brake plates or discs.

An example of a piston rod adjustment type plate brake unit is shown in Fig.3-2. The example shown has four plates or discs and is typical of the type that may be used on medium and large aircraft.

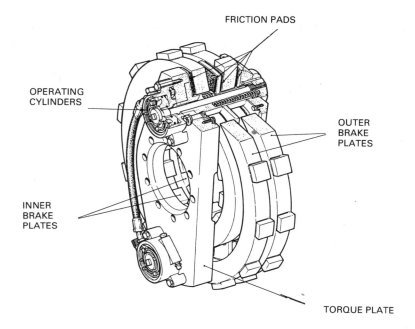

FRICTION PADS

OPERATING
CYLINDERS

OUTER
BRAKE
PLATES

INNER
BRAKE
PLATES

TORQUE PLATE

Fig.3-2. Piston Rod Adjustment Brake Unit.

3.5 The Torque Plate

The torque plate forms the base on which the brake unit is assembled. It carries all the non-rotating parts of the brake unit, such as the operating cylinders and friction pads and also transmits the braking torque to the undercarriage structure. The plate is attached to the undercarriage leg by a ring of bolts located around a central aperture which accommodates the wheel axle. Braking torque is transmitted from the friction pads to the torque plate by two hollow torque pins, located on opposite sides of the central aperture.

3.6 The Operating Cylinders or Actuators

The two operating cylinders are located on the outer face of the torque plate and are centred over the torque pins. The cylinders are tapped to receive a hydraulic oil supply connection and a bleed screw for bleeding off trapped air. A piston housed in each cylinder is moved outward by hydraulic oil under pressure and oil leakage past the piston is prevented by inner and outer sealing rings fitted into grooves in the piston. The outer face of the piston acts on the flanged face or outer end of the piston rod, the stem of which passes through the central standard of the cylinder and then through the hollow torque pin. The inner end of the piston rod is threaded to engage with a special nut which abuts the pressure plate of the inner friction pad.

A square section of the outer end of the piston rod may be turned to alter the amount of engagement of its thread with the special nut. This changes the effective length of the rod and is the means of adjusting the running clearance between the friction pads and the brake plates.

The construction of the brake operating cylinder is shown in Fig.3-3.

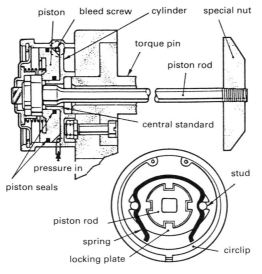

Fig.3-3. Brake Operating Cylinder.

The piston rod type brake unit has one or more sets of brake plates, each set consisting of two separate plates, one inside the other. These separate plates are keyed into the inner and outer locating drive blocks located within the wheel, leaving a space between them for the piston rods of the two diametrically opposed hydraulic operating cylinders. Each piston rod also passes through the centre of a set of friction pads on which it acts when the brakes are applied. Fig.3-4 shows an example of the operating cylinder operation.

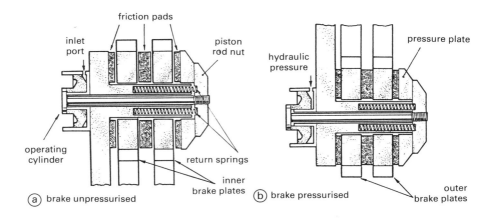

Fig.3-4. Brake Operating Cylinder Operation.

Brakes OFF

The operating cylinder inlet port is open to the hydraulic system return and the brake is 'OFF' as shown at Fig.3-4a. The return springs, by exerting a force on the piston rod nuts are keeping the friction pads out of contact with the rotating brake plates.

Brakes ON

Fig.3-4b shows the brakes 'ON'. Hydraulic pressure, applied at the cylinder inlet by the operation of the brake control valve has forced the piston along the cylinder. The resultant movement has compressed the return springs and pulled the pressure plate between the non-rotating friction pad assemblies. The degree of force applied to the friction pads is controlled by the value of brake pressure which is in turn controlled by the brake control valve.

3.7 Emergency Brake Operation

Most aircraft wheel brake systems are fed by two hydraulic pressure supplies so that braking can continue in the event of a single supply failure. In some versions of the piston rod adjuster type brake unit the two hydraulic pressure supplies are used in a manner as shown in Fig.3-5.

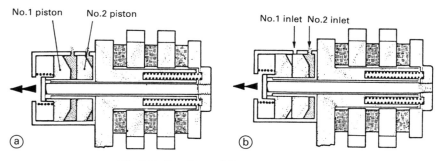

Fig.3-5. Duplicated Pressure Supply.

During normal operation of the brake as shown in Fig.3-5a the pressure is applied to both pistons No.1 and No.2 inlets. Because the pressure acts on both sides of No.2 piston it does not move and the braking effort is produced by the pressure on No.1 piston. If No.1 inlet pressure is lost, as in Fig.3-5b the equalising force on piston No.2 will no longer exist and the piston will be forced into contact with No.1 piston through which the braking force will be transmitted to the piston rod in the usual way.

3.8 Brake Plates

The brake plates fitted to earlier types of aircraft are made of copper and are chromium plated. The chromium skin gives the plates a hard wearing working surface and also increases the efficiency of the brake. The plates on later units are made of steel and do not need to be chromium plated. Fig.3-6 shows a set of brake plates and an example of their location within the wheel. The brake plates shown in Fig.3-6 are of the chromium plated copper type.

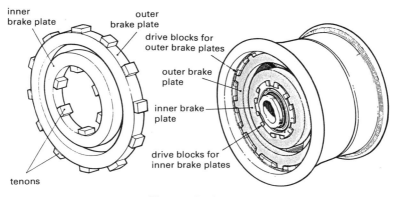

Fig.3-6. Brake Plates.

3.9 Friction Pads

On the example brake unit of the piston rod adjustment type brake unit there are six friction pad assemblies, a set of three at each of the two cylinder positions. The inner and outer pads of each set, which are attached by bolts to a pressure plate and the torque plate respectively, are made up of thin blocks of friction material riveted to one side of a steel backing plate. The third pad, which is located between the two sets of brake plates, consists of a steel carrier plate with blocks of friction material riveted to both sides.

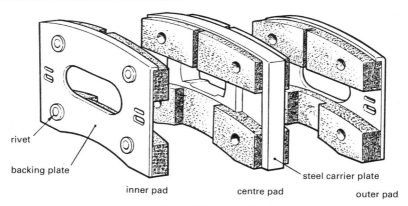

Fig.3-7. Friction Pads.

3.10 The Caliper Type Brake Unit

An example caliper type brake unit is shown in Fig.3-8. This type of brake unit is widely used on lighter types of aircraft and some helicopters.

The essential difference between a caliper type brake unit and a piston rod adjustment brake unit lies in the manner in which the force is applied to the friction pads. With the caliper type the moveable friction pads are pushed towards the fixed friction pads. As shown in Fig.3-8 the caliper brake unit only has one brake plate or disc but may have one set, or several sets of friction pads. The caliper frame is bolted to the undercarriage structure and the plate or disc driven in a similar manner to the brake plates on an adjustable piston rod type brake unit.

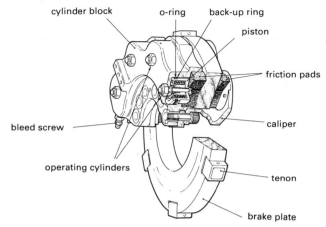

Fig.3-8. Caliper Type Brake Unit.

3.11   The Multi-Segmented Plate Type Brake Unit

Apart from relatively light aircraft, which employ the use of the single plate caliper brake unit, most modern aircraft use the Multi-Segmented Plate Type Brake Unit. An example of this type of unit is shown in Fig.3-9 and consists of the following main component parts:

(a) Torque plate.

(b) Operating cylinders or actuators.

(c) Stator assemblies.

(d) Thrust ring.

(e) Rotor assemblies.

(f) Wear indicators.

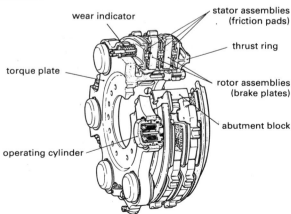

Fig.3-9. Segmented Plate Type Brake Unit.

3.12   Torque Plate

The light alloy torque plate fits over the wheel axle and is attached to the undercarriage structure by a ring of bolts concentric with the axle aperture. The operating cylinders are equally spaced around the torque plate with two additional diametrically opposed housings which accommodate the wear indicators. Projecting inwards from the torque plate is an integral torque tube which has a number of dove-tailed keys machined on its outer periphery. These keys which prevent the stators from rotating and support the rotors, are constructed with wear resistant surfaces.

3.13   Thrust Ring

The thrust ring is bolted to the inner face of the torque tube after the stators (Friction Pads) and rotors (Brake Plates) have been fitted to the brake unit.

3.14   The Operating Cylinders or Actuators

The six operating cylinders are supplied with hydraulic fluid from a common inlet connection via a passage machined into the torque plate. Each cylinder embodies an automatic brake clearance adjuster and consists of a domed liner, a hollow piston and a set of disc return springs known as Schnorr Washers.

Automatic adjustment for brake clearance is affected by the retraction pin, guide, sleeve, distance piece and friction bush which are housed inside the hollow piston. The cylinder liner is drilled to communicate with the oil passage in the torque plate and a ring seal on each side of the piston prevents oil leakage.

An example brake clearance adjuster is shown in Fig.3-10.

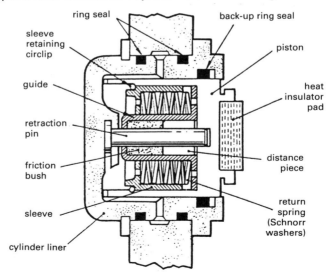

Fig.3-10. Automatic Brake Clearance Adjuster.

3.15 Automatic Brake Adjuster Operation

When the brake pressure is applied to the cylinder, movement of the piston and sleeve compresses the return springs to take up the clearance between the sleeve and the guide. Normally this amount of piston movement is enough to fully apply the brakes. If, however, the stators and rotors have become thinner from wear, more movement will be required to fully apply the brakes and the sleeve will force the guide along the retraction pin against the resistance of the friction bush until full brake application is achieved. When the brake is released the return springs will withdraw the piston and sleeve by a distance equal to the amount the washers or return springs were compressed. This restores the clearance between the sleeve and guide, but the guide remains in its new position on the retraction pin. The brake clearance will therefore be always equal to the design clearance between the sleeve and guide until the friction bush reaches the end of its travel. This will not normally happen within the normal servicing cycle of the brake unit.

3.16 The Rotor Assemblies

The rotor assemblies which correspond to the brake plates of the piston rod adjustment type brake unit, each consist of a number of interlocking steel 'jig-saw' segments as shown in Fig.3-11.

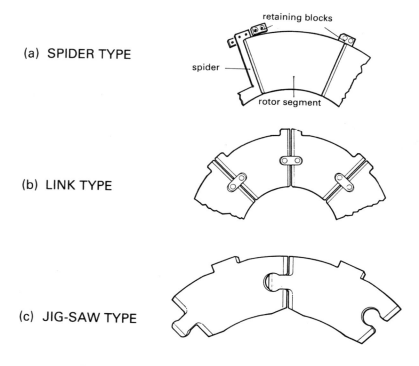

(a) SPIDER TYPE

retaining blocks

spider

rotor segment

(b) LINK TYPE

(c) JIG-SAW TYPE

Fig.3-11. Segmented Brake Plates or Rotors.

Each segment has a tenon machined on its outer edge for engaging with the drive blocks in the wheel rim. The rotors are segmented in this manner to prevent distortion or warping when subjected to high temperatures. By adopting this method of construction the rotors can be manufactured from much thinner steel and therefore are much lighter in weight. Brake development has resulted in three primary methods of producing segmented rotors. They are as follows:

(a) The spider type.

(b) The link type.

(c) The jig-saw type.

Each type is shown in Fig.3-11.

3.17 The Stator Assemblies

The brake unit shown has three stator assemblies, two single stators and one double stator. The single stators operate on the outside faces of the two rotor assemblies and the double stator acts between the two rotors. Each stator consists of an annular plate carrying a number of equally spaced friction pads. The friction pads are each made up of friction material bonded to a carrier plate which is then attached to the annular plate by a single rivet. The slots machined in the annular plates are for keying the stator assemblies to the abutment blocks of the torque tube therefore preventing them from rotating. An example is shown in Fig.3-12.

3.18 The Wear Indicators

The wear indicators provide a visual indication of the brake unit friction surface wear by gauging the reduction in total thickness of the stators and rotors. They do this by recording the increasing amount by which the pressure plate has to be moved away from the torque plate before the stators and rotors are clamped together to apply the brake. Each of the two indicators consist of an internally threaded indicator sleeve secured in position by a bolt and locknut as shown in Fig.3-13. Wear indicators vary in design but all essentially perform the same function.

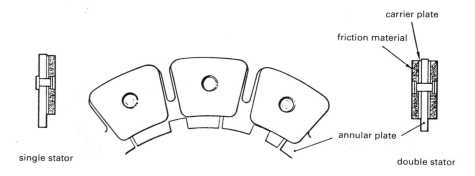

Fig.3-12. Stator Assembly.

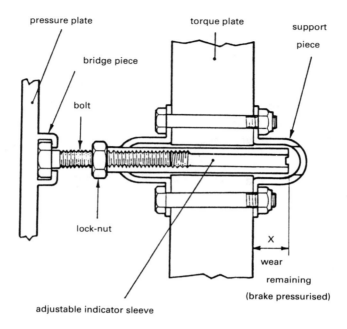

Fig.3-13. Wear Indicator.

TEST YOURSELF 3
BRAKE UNITS

1. The tenons of a brake plate:
    (a) are located between the drive blocks of the wheel.
    (b) are fitted to reduce warping due to high temperatures.
    (c) are used to balance the rotor.
    (d) are driven by the tyre bead.

    Ref. 3.3.

2. The brake plates of a piston rod adjuster type brake unit are manufactured from:
    (a) steel.
    (b) steel coated with chromium.
    (c) copper.
    (d) copper coated with chromium.

    Ref. 3.8.

3. Caliper brake units are used:
    (a) on light aircraft.
    (b) where high temperatures are encountered.
    (c) on large aircraft only.
    (d) on helicopters only.

    Ref. 3.10.

4. The stator of a modern brake unit is the:
    (a) brake plate.
    (b) friction pads.
    (c) torque plate.
    (d) caliper.

    Ref. 3.11.

5. Modern brake discs are segmented to:
    (a) reduce the tendency to warp.
    (b) prevent excessive wear.
    (c) allow them to be made thicker.
    (d) reduce brake temperature.

    Ref. 3.16.

6. An alternative name given to the segmented type brake unit is:
   (a) a heat pack.
   (b) a caliper brake unit.
   (c) a drum brake.
   (d) a spider brake.

Ref. 3.3.

7. A jig-saw assembly is a term applied to a:
   (a) segmented rotor.
   (b) segmented stator.
   (c) caliper brake.
   (d) brake adjuster.

Ref. 3.16.

8. The drive blocks are:
   (a) mounted on the wheel axle.
   (b) mounted on the rotor.
   (c) mounted on the wheel rim.
   (d) mounted on the stator.

Ref. 3.16.

9. The rotors of a modern segmented brake unit are manufactured from:
   (a) copper.
   (b) chromium.
   (c) light alloy.
   (d) steel.

Ref. 3.16.

10. Wear indicators provide an indication of wear by:
    (a) a warning light in the cockpit.
    (b) a visual indication on the brake unit.
    (c) a visual indication on the instrument panel.
    (d) a visual indication on the brake rotor.

Ref. 3.18.

4

AIRCRAFT WHEELS

4.1 Introduction

Aircraft wheels are manufactured from aluminium alloy or magnesium alloy and are given treatment to protect them from corrosion as well as a paint finish. It is important that the paint finish and anti-corrosive treatments are kept in good order to prevent the onset of corrosion in the wheel. An aircraft wheel is subjected to considerable stress during its normal operational life and in the area of the brake units on the main wheels is also subjected to high temperature. Wheels that are fitted with tubeless tyres must also be made airtight.

4.2 Basic Construction

It is an advantage to the pilot to know the basic construction of an aircraft wheel in order he may evaluate the limitations that may be imposed on a wheel in the event of some types of damage. The wheel consists of three basic parts which are as follows:

(a) A hub which carries the wheel bearing.

(b) Solid spokes which are usually in the form of a single ventilated disc.

(c) A flanged rim on which the tyre is fitted.

Fig.4-1 shows the basic parts of an aircraft wheel.

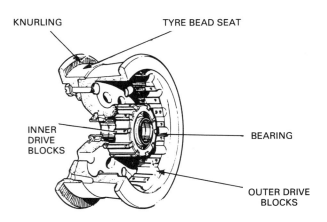

Fig.4-1. A Basic Aircraft Wheel.

Main, nose and tail wheels are similar in construction, except that the main wheels have a recess in one, or both, sides to house a brake assembly. It should be noted that few aircraft have brake units fitted to nose or tail wheel assemblies.

A typical wheel is shown in Fig.4-2.

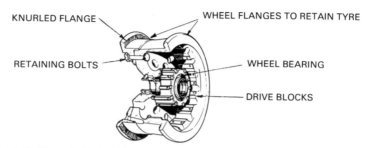

KNURLED FLANGE

WHEEL FLANGES TO RETAIN TYRE

RETAINING BOLTS

WHEEL BEARING

DRIVE BLOCKS

Fig.4-2. Aircraft Main Wheel Assembly, for a Tubed Tyre Assembly.

The wheel shown in Fig.4-2 is manufactured in two main parts and is known as a divided wheel. Each half is attached to the other and retained by a series of bolts. The wheel is manufactured in this way to allow for an easier tyre change by the engineers when the wheel is serviced. The wheel has two flanges to retain the tyre in place. Note that the flanges have a knurled face, a roughened type of finish; this is to assist in preventing the tyre creeping on the wheel, particularly when the brakes are applied. Tyre creep is also minimised by the bead seat, which is slightly tapered so that when the tyre is fitted, and inflated, the tyre bead is forced out toward the flange over the tapered bead seat, which produces a very tight fit so helping to prevent creep.

As can be seen in Fig.4-2 on the inner face, or inner side of the wheel, that is the side of the wheel which faces the undercarriage leg are what are termed drive blocks. These are blocks of metal that are bolted to the wheel and engage with the brake rotor, or disc, and as the wheel rotates so the drive blocks drive the disc or rotor of the brake unit.

In the centre of the hub are housed the wheel bearings which are normally of the ball or roller type.

Fig.4-3 is an extension of Fig.4-2 showing the same wheel related to its brake unit.

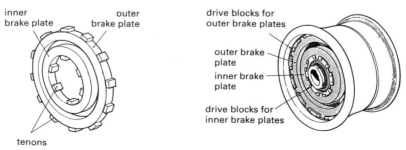

inner
brake plate

outer
brake plate

drive blocks for
outer brake plates

outer brake
plate

inner brake
plate

drive blocks for
inner brake plates

tenons

Fig.4-3. Wheel Assembly and Brake Unit for a Tubed Tyre Assembly.

4.3   Tubeless Tyre Wheel Assembly

If a wheel is to be used with a tubeless tyre then the wheel itself must complete the airtight compartment. The tubeless tyre is shown in Fig.4-4.

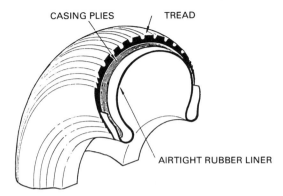

Fig.4-4. The Air Compartment with a Tubeless Tyre.

The example discussed in this section is also a divided wheel which again is manufactured in two major sections, or halves and bolted together by a series of bolts.

The major difference with this type is as it is fitted with a tubeless tyre the two halves of the wheel must be sealed to prevent the escape of air through the joint. This is normally achieved with the use of a rubber sealing ring. It must be remembered the metal is not airtight and the surface between the flanges must also be sealed. The metal surface between the flanges is coated with a resin to prevent the permeation of air through the metal.

Fig.4-5 shows an example of a wheel assembly designed for a tubeless tyre. It should be noted a knurled flange is not used on this type of wheel, creep is reduced by the tapered bead seat coupled with the correct tyre pressure.

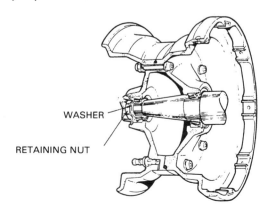

Fig.4-5. Tubeless Tyre Wheel.

4.4 Wheel Bearings

The wheel bearings are normally of a ball or roller type. As has been seen in previous illustrations the bearing is normally housed in the wheel hub.

The bearing consists of three main parts, the outer race, the inner race and the ball or roller race.

Fig.4-6 shows an example of a roller bearing assembly.

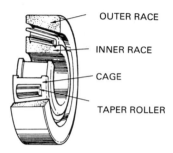

OUTER RACE

INNER RACE

CAGE

TAPER ROLLER

Fig.4-6. A Typical Roller Wheel Bearing.

Most modern aircraft main wheels are retained on the axle by a single main wheel nut; the nut in turn is locked. The wheel nut is not normally screwed on tight as a small amount of clearance must be left to allow for expansion due to the high temperatures that tend to be generated within the wheel bearing. The bearings are normally lubricated by grease which is packed in the bearing at the time it is fitted to the wheel.

Servicing of wheel bearings is the responsibility of the engineer, however a working knowledge of the wheel assembly is an advantage to the pilot.

4.5 Fusible Alloy Plugs

The majority of tubeless tyre main wheels are fitted with small pressure relief valves which are known as fusible alloy plugs. In the event a tubeless tyre is subjected to excessive heat due to heavy wheel braking there is a danger the tyre may blow out. In the event a blow out should occur, loss of control of the aircraft during the landing run may follow. To avoid this situation it is better to slowly deflate the tyre, relieving the excess pressure whilst maintaining control of the aircraft. This is the main objective of the fusible alloy plug.

The fusible alloy plug is retained in the wheel by a screw thread and is located between the flanges or wheel rims. In the event the temperature of the air exceeds a certain value a fusible alloy in the centre of the plug melts and slowly allows the air to escape, giving a controlled deflation of the tyre thereby preventing the tyre from bursting or blowing out. Some wheels may be fitted with a series of fusible alloy plugs located at various points around the wheel and normally set to melt at different temperatures.

Generally there may be one or a combination of three temperature settings employed on a wheel. The common temperatures at which fusible alloy plugs melt are as follows:

(a) 155 degrees centigrade — plug body coloured red.

(b) 177 degrees centigrade — plug body coloured green.

(c) 199 degrees centigrade — plug body coloured yellow.

Fig.4-7 shows an example of a fusible alloy plug.

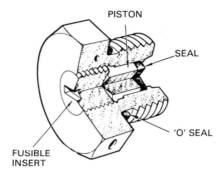

Fig.4-7. Fusible Alloy Plug.

In the event any tyre is deflated during the landing run, and any tyre on the same axle, then the tyres are automatically scrapped. This means that regardless of whether the tyres on the same axle are deflated or not the tyres are all scrapped.

TEST YOURSELF 4
AIRCRAFT WHEELS

1. In a divided type aircraft wheel which is designed to be fitted with a tubeless tyre:
   (a) a seal is fitted between the two halves.
   (b) seals are not required between the wheel halves.
   (c) resin is used to seal the two halves of the wheel.
   (d) a rubber seal is fitted to prevent air permeating through the metal.

                                                            Ref. 4.3.

2. When a fusible alloy plug melts:
   (a) the tyre deflates rapidly.
   (b) the tyre deflates slowly.
   (c) the tyre is partially deflated.
   (d) the brake cooling fan is activated.

                                                            Ref. 4.5.

3. The type of bearing most commonly used on aircraft wheels is:
   (a) ball or roller type.
   (b) plain bearing.
   (c) shell bearing.
   (d) white metal bearing.

                                                            Ref. 4.4.

4. Aircraft wheels are normally manufactured from:
   (a) steel.
   (b) stainless steel.
   (c) nimonic alloy.
   (d) aluminium or magnesium alloy.

                                                            Ref. 4.1.

5. Fusible alloy plugs:
   (a) are only fitted to tubed tyre wheel assemblies.
   (b) may be fitted to tubeless or tubed wheel assemblies.
   (c) are only fitted to tubeless tyre wheel assemblies.
   (d) are only fitted to tail wheels.

                                                            Ref. 4.5.

6. A red fusible alloy plug is designed to melt at:
    (a) 199 degrees centigrade.
    (b) 177 degrees centigrade.
    (c) 155 degrees centigrade.
    (d) 166 degrees centigrade.

                                        Ref. 4.5.

7. On a wheel designed to take a tubed tyre, creep is minimised by:
    (a) drive blocks.
    (b) knurled flange.
    (c) bolts.
    (d) valve stems.

                                        Ref. 4.2.

8. Drive blocks are fitted to wheels to:
    (a) drive the brake disc or rotor.
    (b) act as an anti-creep device.
    (c) act as a retaining device for the tyre.
    (d) eject water from the tread on landing.

                                        Ref. 4.2.

9. The wheel bearing is normally lubricated by:
    (a) oil from the engine lubrication system.
    (b) self contained oil.
    (c) self contained silicon.
    (d) grease packed on assembly.

                                        Ref. 4.4.

10. A clearance is established at the main wheel nut on fitting the wheel
    to the axle to:
    (a) allow for creep.
    (b) allow for expansion.
    (c) allow for easier wheel replacement.
    (d) allow the brake unit to cool.

                                        Ref. 4.4.

5

AIRCRAFT TYRES

5.1 Introduction

The major loads which have to be taken by an aircraft tyre are somewhat different to those taken by an average road vehicle. The aircraft tyre is subjected to very high impact loads which will occur at the touch-down on landing. Also during the landing run the prolonged action of the wheel brakes will cause a considerable build up of temperature, much of which will be felt by the tyre through the wheel from the brake unit. In general the aircraft tyre has to be constructed more strongly and from rubber which can withstand high temperatures but can be constructed as light as possible.

5.2 The Function of the Tyre

The primary function of aircraft tyres is to support the aircraft on the ground and to absorb part of the shocks from landing and taxying. The other functions of the tyre are as follows:

(a) To provide gripping power when in contact with the ground for braking and steering.

(b) To provide an easily replaceable wearing surface.

(c) May provide an electrical contact with the ground for discharging static electricity. Only one tyre needs this capability per aircraft, although on most aircraft all types are electrically conducting.

To achieve its primary functions, the tyre is filled with compressed air or nitrogen to act as a cushion. For most tyres the gas is retained, in conjunction with a suitably sealed wheel, by the tyre itself. However, on some tyres, usually those fitted to older types of aircraft, which, because of their construction, are difficult to seal, the compressed air or nitrogen is retained in an inner tube.

Note: The use of nitrogen on modern aircraft tyres is very common to assist in preventing a fire in the event of a 'blow out'.

5.3 Tubed Tyre Construction.

The construction of a tubed tyre, basically, consists of a rubber casing, which is usually treaded and is reinforced on the inside with successive layers of closely spaced nylon cords. Each layer is known as a ply. The cords of a ply are not interwoven but lie parallel to each other in a single tier and are held together by a thin film of rubber. This rubber also serves to prevent the cords of adjacent plies cutting into each other as the tyre flexes in use. Plies run diagonally across the tyre and are arranged so that there is an angle between adjacent plies of 90 degrees.

Fig.5-1 shows the construction of a tubed tyre.

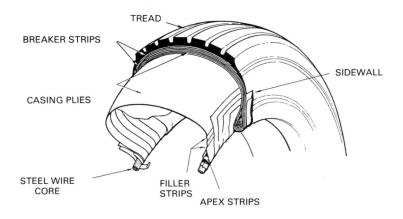

Fig.5-1. Tubed Tyre Construction.

5.4   Component Parts of a Tubed Tyre

(a) Breaker Strips

The purpose of the breaker strips is to spread the loads on the tread area of the tyre. Two or more further plies are embedded in a thicker film of rubber, which are incorporated between the outer ply and the casing rubber. These special plies are known as breaker strips.

(b) Bead Wires

The casing plies are overlapped at each side of the casing around one or more bead wires. These bead wires strengthen the tyre and retain it on the wheel rim. The bead wire consists of several individual wires made from high tensile steel which are copper plated to ensure an effective bond between the rubber and the steel. A strip of fabric is spirally wound on to each bead wire to prevent it from damaging the cords.

(c) Apex Strips and Filler Strips

The rubber apex strips and rubberised fabric filler strips provide a bonding medium for the plies in what would otherwise be an abrupt change in section behind the bead wires.

(d) Chafer Strips

Chafer strips are made of rubberised fabric and they provide additional protection for the plies where the tyre is in contact with the wheel rim at the tyre beads.

(e) Fabric Reinforcement

On many high speed tyres it is common practice to include one layer of fabric in the tyre casing to reinforce the tread rubber. In some instances the fabric is in the tread area of the tyre which will tend to become exposed as the tyre progressively wears. This exposed fabric must not be confused with the actual plies of the tyre. The exposing of the reinforced fabric is part of the normal wear process. Some tyres of this type that are currently being manu-factured may have more than one layer of reinforcing fabric.

Fig.5-2 shows two variations of reinforced fabric within the tyre construction.

Fig.5-2. Reinforced Fabric Tread.

5.5 Tubeless Tyre Construction

The construction of a tubeless tyre is similar to the tubed tyre. The primary difference in their construction is the elimination of a separate tube and the inclusion of a liner bonded to the inner plies which makes the structure airtight.

The lining which retains the pressurised air or nitrogen in the tyre, extends around the tyre beads to provide a gas-tight seal between the tyre and the wheel rim and flanges.

An example of a tubeless tyre is shown in Fig.5-3.

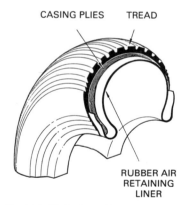

CASING PLIES   TREAD

RUBBER AIR
RETAINING
LINER

Fig.5-3. Tubeless Tyre Construction.

5.6 Advantages of a Tubeless Tyre

Compared with a tubed tyre, the tubeless tyre has the following advantages:

(a) There is less deflation risk from punctures. Unlike a tubed tyre the rubber lining of the tyre is unstretched and will cling closely, and remain sealed, around the puncturing object.

(b) As there is no heat generation from friction between the tyre and tube the assembly is cooler running.

(c) As there is no tube fitted there is a considerable weight saving.

5.7 Regions of a Tyre

For the purpose of description, a tyre is divided into regions as shown in Fig.5-4.

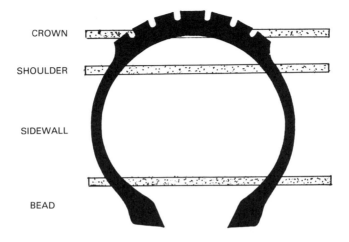

CROWN

SHOULDER

SIDEWALL

BEAD

Fig.5-4. Regions of a Tyre.

5.8 Tyre Treads

The tread area of a tyre provides an indication of wear, grip, and a means of displacing water. The majority of tyres fall into two types of tread pattern which are:

(a) Block Pattern

The treads of these tyres takes the form of raised blocks which may be square, circular or diamond shaped. In wet conditions, the blocks squeeze the water into the spaces between them leaving a comparatively dry area of runway for the tread to grip on.

Examples of block tread patterns are shown in Fig.5-5.

Fig.5-5. Block Tread Tyres.

(b) Ribbed Tyres

This type of tread pattern is the most widely used of tread types. They combine a non-skid characteristic with a low rolling resistance and good directional stability. Fig.5-6 shows examples of ribbed tread patterns.

Fig.5-6. Ribbed Tread Patterns.

5.9 Specialist Tyre Treads

There are a number of special types of tyre tread to satisfy specialist requirements. Some such types are discussed below.

(a) The Chined Tyre

Chined tyres are normally treaded but, in addition, have a rubber flange, or chine, protruding outwards from one, or both, of the tyre sidewalls just below the shoulder. The purpose of the chine is to deflect any spray thrown out by the tyre tread away from the aircraft structure. This type of tyre is often fitted to nose wheels to reduce the amount of water being thrown aft into engine intakes.

Fig.5-7 shows an example of a chined tyre.

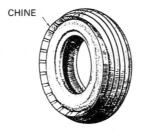

CHINE

Fig.5-7. A Chined Tyre.

(b) Anti-Shimmy Tyres

On large aircraft, nose-wheel shimmy is prevented by a shimmy damper, or by the use of twin wheels. Shimmy is the oscillation of the wheel assembly from side to side which normally occurs at relatively low speeds during the landing run.

A two-wheeled nose undercarriage will prevent this action; however, on some aircraft a single tyre which provides a twin contact may be used. This type of tyre is also known as a 'Marstrand Tyre' named after its inventor. An example is shown in Fig.5-8.

Fig.5-8. A Marstrand Tyre.

5.10 Tyre Markings

Aircraft tyres have certain markings imprinted on the sidewall of the tyre for identification purposes. These markings vary according to the manufacturer but generally include the following standard markings:

(a) Size.

(b) Part Number.

(c) Serial Number.

(d) Date of Manufacture.

(e) Tubed or Tubeless.

(f) Speed Rating.

(g) Ply Rating.

(h) The Type and Number of Retreads carried out.

5.11 Tyre Size Markings

Tyres are identified for size in the following manner:

For example 26 × 10.00 − 18

26   − indicates the outside diameter of the tyre.

10.00 − indicates the inside diameter of the tyre.

18   − indicates the bead diameter of the tyre.

See Fig.5-9.

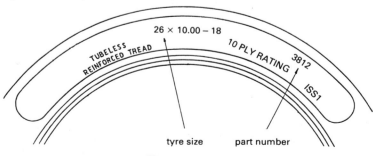

Fig.5-9. Tyre Size.

It will be found that not all tyres specify all three dimensions. Some American tyres may only quote the outside diameter and the width size, or the width of the tyre and the bead or internal diameter. To assist in identifying which sizes are being indicated the following practice is standard:

(a) Where the size is shown as 26 × 10.00 only, the figure followed by the symbol × must be the outside diameter of the tyre.

(b) Where the dimension is preceded by the symbol × the dimension must be the width of the tyre.

(c) Where the dimension is preceded by the – symbol this must be the bead diameter.

5.12 The Tyre Part Number

The part number includes the manufacturer's identification, the drawing number to which the tyre is manufactured and letters to indicate the tread type and whether it is a tubed or tubeless tyre. The part number is the only positive means of identifying a tyre. Size markings alone does *not* identify a tyre as being suitable for a given purpose.

An example of a part number is:

DR7152 T

D	is the manufacturer.
R	means it has a ribbed tread.
7152	is the drawing number.
T	indicates it's a tubed tyre.

5.13 Serial Number

The serial number is normally marked in conjunction with the date of manufacture. This is sometimes indicated in the form of a code.

An example of a serial number is:

2283 Nov 72 or 2302283.

5.14 Ply Rating

This is an important marking on a tyre and is used to identify a tyre with its maximum recommended load and pressure. It is an index of the tyre strength and does not necessarily represent the number of cord plies used in the construction of the tyre.

An example of the ply rating markings may be as follows:

10 ply rating written in full or abbreviated to 10PR.

5.15 Speed Rating

Most high speed tyres, that is those tyres which may be used at speeds over 160 miles per hour have the speed rating imprinted on the wall of the tyre. The speed indicated on the tyre is the maximum speed for which the tyre is designed.

5.16 Other Markings

The following are some of the additional markings found on aircraft tyres which are of importance to the pilot's knowledge.

(a) Awl Vents

These are small holes which are put into the tyre casing to allow trapped air to escape from between the cord layers during manufacture and are usually identified by small green or grey dots.

(b) The Light Part of the Tyre

This is indicated by a single red dot, or triangle, which for engineering purposes shows the light part of the tyre.

(c) Retreads

Retreaded tyres are marked with a system of markings peculiar to a particular manufacturer.

5.17 High Pressure Tyres

Some aircraft tyres are inflated to pressures in the order of 1400 kN/m^2 (200lbf/in^2) or more. These tyres are termed High Pressure Tyres.

5.18 Tyre Creep

Tyre creep is the tendency of the tyre to slip or creep on the wheel or to physically rotate about the wheel. If this should occur damage may be caused to the bead of the tyre and in the case of a tubed tyre may cause the inflation valve to be broken off from the tube causing a blow-out of the tyre assembly. Various methods are employed to minimise creep such as:

(a) A knurled flange on a tubed assembly.

(b) A tapered bead seat on the wheel.

(c) Ensuring the correct tyre pressure is maintained.

5.19 Tyre Creep Marks

In addition to the tyre markings previously mentioned in this chapter most tyres have moulded creep marks on the side wall of the tyre in the bead region. The moulded marks consist of two arrows set a specific distance apart, the distance being dependent upon the size of the tyre.

The spacing of the arrows determine the width of the creep marks. The width of the creep marks must be:

(a) 25mm (1″) for tyres up to 600mm (24″) nominal outside diameter.

(b) 38mm (1.5″) for tyres over 600mm (24″) nominal outside diameter.

Normally when the tyre is fitted to the wheel the space between the arrows is painted white with a corresponding white band on the wheel rim. When the assembly is first inflated the two white marks are in line with each other. In service any tendency of the tyre to creep will be indicated by the creep marks moving out of line with each other. The width of the creep marks indicates the maximum circumferential movement of the tyre permitted on a tubed tyre.

Creep on tubeless tyres is not considered to be a serious problem provided the bead region of the tyre is not damaged.

See Fig.5-10.

NO CREEP   MAXIMUM CREEP

Fig.5-10. Tyre Creep Marks.

5.20 Tyre Wear

(a) Examination

A careful visual examination of tyres must be carried out prior to each flight, rotating the wheels wherever possible to ensure that the whole surface of the tyre is checked. Manufacturers advise limits of damage within which a tyre may be kept in service; tyres damaged in excess of these limits should be removed from the aircraft and repaired or scrapped as appropriate. The following paragraphs list some of the possible faults and the action to be taken.

(b) Embedded Stones, Flints and Glass

The outer surface of the tyre should be examined for embedded objects and any found should be carefully removed.

(c) Cuts and Scores

All cuts should be probed with a suitable blunt tool in order to assess the depth and extent of any damage to the casing. Minor damage may be defined as that which does not affect the casing cords. Cuts in the tread and side rubber, providing they do not expose the casing cord, do not appreciably weaken the tyre.

(d) Bulges

The presence of bulges may indicate a partial failure of the casing and the tyre should be removed for further examination by the engineer.

(e) Tyre Wear

The extent to which tread has been removed from a tyre is not always easy to assess and may be general or local wear. Some of the more important methods of wear indication are shown in Fig.5-11.

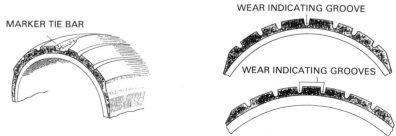

MARKER TIE BAR

WEAR INDICATING GROOVE

WEAR INDICATING GROOVES

Fig.5-11. Tyre Wear Indication.

Local wear may be in the form of a 'Flat Spot' caused by severe abrasion or skid burns and these may occur as a result of excessive braking, hard landings or aquaplaning. The probability of aquaplaning increases as the depth of tread is reduced. It is recommended that tyres be removed when wear has reached the limits as listed below:

(a) Pattern tread tyres may be used until the tread is worn to the depth of the pattern.

(b) Ribbed tyres with marker tie bars may be used until worn to the top of the marker tie bars.

(c) Ribbed tyres without marker tie bars may be used until worn to within 2mm (0.080″) of the bottom of the wear indicator groove.

(d) Twin contact tyres (Marstrand tyres) may be used until the centre of the crown of the tyre shows signs of being in contact with the ground.

(e) Plain tyres as seen rarely on some types of older aircraft may be used until the cushion rubber or cords are exposed.

It should be noted on tyres with reinforced treads, several layers of fabric are moulded into the tread rubber and will become visible during normal operational wear: this fabric must not be confused with the casing cords, or plies. Normally these tyres are fitted with marker tie bars which should be used to determine the wear as shown in Fig.5-11.

5.21   Tyre Pressures

The importance of keeping the tyres inflated to the correct pressure cannot be overstressed. Under-inflated tyres may creep to such an extent that the inflation valve assembly may be torn out of the tube, causing the tyre to deflate rapidly and loss of control of the aircraft may follow. Over-inflated tyres can cause excessive vibration when taxying, or rolling on the ground which can lead to structural damage. Over-inflated tyres may also lead to excessive or uneven wear and may lead to high pressure bursts. It should also be noted where there are two tyres mounted on the same axle, uneven tyre pressures may lead to one tyre carrying a greater load than the other which may result in one of the tyres operating above its rated specification; this may also cause excessive stress to the undercarriage unit.

The manufacturers of tyres specify a rated inflation pressure for each tyre, which applies to a cold tyre not carrying any load. The pressure to which a tyre should be inflated when it is subjected to aircraft weight, is determined by adding a pressure allowance (normally 4 per cent) to the rated inflation pressure. A tolerance of 5 per cent to 10 per cent above the loaded inflation pressure is generally specified and tyre pressures up to this maximum are permitted and may benefit tyre reliability. The loaded inflation tyre pressures for the tyres on a particular aircraft are normally specified in the aircraft maintenance manual as the maximum and minimum pressures permitted, or it may be shown in the form of a graph with pressure related to aircraft weight.

After an aircraft has landed, or has been subjected to prolonged taxying, individual tyre pressures may vary because of the energy absorbed by the tyre and heat transfer from the brake units and a pressure increase of up to 10 per cent can be expected. This pressure should not be reduced to normal values as this could lead, after the tyre has cooled down to an under-inflated tyre.

5.22 Conducting Tyres

During flight and or when an aircraft is being fuelled, or de-fuelled, considerable static electricity may build up within the aircraft which may lead to a potential difference between the aircraft and the ground or other items of equipment adjacent to the aircraft when it is parked on the ground being serviced. It is essential that in the event there is such a build-up of static electricity that it is immediately earthed to avoid any sparks or arcing. To achieve this, aircraft tyres must be capable of conducting electricity and a mandatory requirement is that either the nose or tail wheel are electrically conducting tyres. In reality most tyres used on aircraft are electrically conducting including those fitted to main wheels.

To this end electrically conducting tyres are clearly marked to show they are constructed to carry out this function. There are three common methods of marking conducting tyres; these marks are shown in Fig-5.12.

(a) The word CONDUCTING.

(b) The letters ECTA – Electrically Conducting Tyre Assembly.

(c) The symbol –

Fig.5-12. Electrically Conducting Markings.

TEST YOURSELF 5
AIRCRAFT TYRES

1. A major advantage of a Tubeless Tyre is:
   - (a) it cannot possibly leak or deflate.
   - (b) it is heavier in construction.
   - (c) less heat is generated within the tyre.
   - (d) the tyre may be made smaller.

   Ref. 5.6.

2. A Chined Tyre is used on some modern aircraft to:
   - (a) reduce wear.
   - (b) spread the load over a greater area.
   - (c) deflect water spray.
   - (d) allow a greater landing speed.

   Ref. 5.9a.

3. A Chined Tyre is normally fitted to:
   - (a) light aircraft only.
   - (b) main wheels only.
   - (c) aircraft using grass strips.
   - (d) nose undercarriages.

   Ref. 5.9a.

4. A 'Marstrand Tyre' is:
   - (a) another name for a chined tyre.
   - (b) another name for a tubeless tyre.
   - (c) a cordless tyre.
   - (d) a twin contact tyre.

   Ref. 5.9b.

5. Twin contact tyres are used to:
   - (a) reduce tyre wear.
   - (b) reduce shimmy.
   - (c) spread the load over a greater area.
   - (d) reduce aircraft weight.

   Ref. 5.9b.

6. On an aircraft tyre with the size marked as 32 × 12.00 – 8 the first numbers '32' indicate:
   (a) the internal diameter.
   (b) the bead diameter.
   (c) the width of the tyre.
   (d) the overall diameter.

Ref. 5.11.

7. The Ply Rating of a tyre as marked on the side wall indicates:
   (a) the number of plies per inch.
   (b) the total number of plies.
   (c) the strength of the tyre.
   (d) the number of plies in a given layer.

Ref. 5.14.

8. Awl Vents are identified by:
   (a) small red dots on the tyre wall.
   (b) small grey dots on the tyre.
   (c) small yellow dots on the tyre.
   (d) code numbers only.

Ref. 5.16a.

9. The light spot of a tyre is indicated by:
   (a) a yellow dot.
   (b) a grey dot.
   (c) a green dot.
   (d) a red dot.

Ref. 5.16b.

10. The speed rating of a tyre is indicated as:
    (a) the average landing speed permitted.
    (b) the maximum all-up-weight permitted.
    (c) the maximum speed permitted.
    (d) the minimum speed for take-off.

Ref. 5.15.

6

WHEEL BRAKE
OPERATING SYSTEM

6.1 Introduction

The majority of modern aircraft wheel brakes are operated by hydraulic actuation both for normal operation and for emergency. The fluid under pressure for normal operation is provided by the main hydraulic supply system. For emergency operation hydraulic accumulators are provided.

6.2 Basic Wheel Brake Hydraulic System

Fig.6-1 shows a simple wheel brake system as used on many light aircraft. The system comprises a hydraulic supply, normally provided by an engine-driven pump, which on entering the brake system passes through a non-return valve to the brake control valve. The non-return valve creates a safety situation in that fluid under pressure which has entered the system cannot flow back into the hydraulic supply, or be influenced by the operation of other hydraulic sub-systems.

After passing through the non-return valve the fluid is directed through the pipelines to the brake control valve. The brake control valve is operated by the pilot by foot pedals, situated on the rudder bar, or by a brake lever which may be located on the control column. Most modern wheel brakes are operated by foot pedals. In the system shown in Fig.6-1 Foot Pedal Operation is employed. Operation of the foot pedals, or brake pedals controls the brake control valve.

The brake control valve performs a number of functions:

(a) To reduce the hydraulic supply system pressure to a lower value by a pressure reducing valve located within the brake control valve. Generally, supply system pressure would be too high which would cause the braking to be too harsh.

(b) The second function the brake control valve provides is the ability to employ progressive braking on the landing run. Progressive braking is the progressive selection of increased brake pressure as speed reduces on the landing run. By having the ability to vary the brake pressure as required better control can be achieved.

(c) The third primary function the brake control valve provides is the ability to use differential braking when required. Differential braking is the application of separate, or individual brakes in order to achieve steering through the wheel brakes. This practice is widely employed on lighter types of aircraft. Larger aircraft tend to be equipped with nose wheel steering.

When brakes are selected fluid is directed to the wheel brake units. The degree of braking required is achieved by the amount the brake pedals are depressed. The further the pedals are depressed the greater the degree of braking achieved. Progressive braking can be obtained by progressive depression of the pedals. Differential braking can be obtained by application of one brake or the other as required.

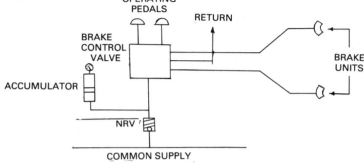

Fig.6-1. Simple Wheel Brake System.

6.3 The Brake Accumulator

During normal brake operation when brakes are selected an instant supply of fluid under pressure is required; this is initially provided by the brake accumulator. If the supply system provided the sole supply of hydraulic fluid under pressure there may be a delay while the main supply system pump builds up sufficient pressure to operate the brakes. Such an important system as the wheel brakes cannot rely solely on pump supply. The main supply pump will continuously recharge the accumulator with system fluid pressure but in each case of brake application the accumulator will supply the initial application of the brakes, in other words, provide the initial impetus.

In the event of main system supply failure the accumulator will provide a source of hydraulic fluid under pressure for emergency operation of the wheel brakes. The accumulator is so designed to provide sufficient pressure in an emergency to operate the wheel brakes for a complete landing run plus a reserve.

Further details of accumulator operations are given in Volume 5 of this series of guides.

6.4 Operation of the Brake Control Valve

The brake control valve is operated on most modern aircraft by servo pressure. The servo pressure is generated by the force being applied to the brake pedals which in turn operates a master cylinder. The master cylinder generates pressure which is transmitted via a flexible hose to a servo, or slave cylinder. The servo cylinder converts the pressure energy back into mechanical energy and operates the brake control valve.

It must be noted the fluid within the servo system is totally independent of the main supply fluid and to this end a filler point is usually provided at the master cylinder to top up the servo system when required.

Fig.6-2 shows the servo system in its basic form.

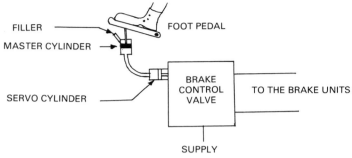

Fig.6-2. Basic Servo System.

Details of the operation of the brake control valve are given in Volume 5 of this series of guides.

6.5 Brake Operation

Brakes are applied by depression of the brake pedals by which, via the servo system, the brake control valve is operated, initially directing fluid from the brake accumulator to the wheel brake units. As the fluid passes through the control valve the system pressure is reduced to a lower value. Fluid is directed to the brake unit inlet and then to the brake unit operating cylinders. It should be noted that unlike some other systems, the amount of fluid flow to actually apply the brakes is quite small. When brakes are released the fluid normally flows from the brake unit back to the brake control valve and then to return, i.e. back to the reservoir. The accumulator in the meantime is re-pressurised with system fluid ready for further brake applications.

6.6 Anti-Skid Unit

If an anti-skid unit is fitted to the system it is located between the brake control valve and the brake unit. Further details of the anti-skid unit and its function within the system are given in Chapter 7.

Fig.6-3 shows the wheel brake hydraulic system.

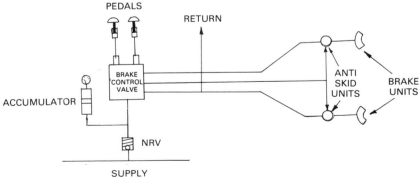

Fig.6-3. Hydraulic Brake System.

TEST YOURSELF 6
WHEEL BRAKE OPERATING SYSTEM

1. The supply of hydraulic pressure when wheel brakes are applied is provided by:
   - (a) servo pressure.
   - (b) supply pressure.
   - (c) accumulator pressure.
   - (d) mechanical pressure.

   Ref. 6.5.

2. The brake control valve is operated by:
   - (a) mechanical force.
   - (b) servo pressure.
   - (c) system pressure.
   - (d) accumulator pressure.

   Ref. 6.5.

3. An anti-skid unit when fitted is located between:
   - (a) the brake unit and the wheel.
   - (b) the brake control valve and the brake unit.
   - (c) the accumulator and the brake control valve.
   - (d) the master cylinder and the servo cylinder.

   Ref. 6.6.

4. When brake pressure is released the fluid returns:
   - (a) directly from the brake unit to the reservoir.
   - (b) via the brake control valve.
   - (c) via the brake accumulator.
   - (d) via the servo system.

   Ref. 6.5.

5. Fluid for the servo system is:
   - (a) supplied by the main system reservoir.
   - (b) supplied by the accumulator.
   - (c) self-contained in the servo system.
   - (d) supplied by the main system accumulator.

   Ref. 6.4.

7

BRAKE UNIT
ANTI-SKID SYSTEMS

7.1 Introduction

Maximum retardation of an aircraft wheel is achieved when the braking force is at its maximum just prior to the wheel locking, or ceasing to rotate. This is sometimes difficult to achieve without the use of some form of automatic braking control. Once the wheel locks or skids, only the tyre in contact with the ground is generating friction and so the braking effort is reduced. Also if the wheel is allowed to lock, control of the aircraft becomes more difficult, causes excessive wear to the tyres and should a blow-out of the tyres occur, total loss of control may result.

The Anti-Skid Unit is fitted to achieve maximum retardation of the wheel brakes without the wheel skidding, the general result being:

(a) Reduced tyre wear.

(b) Shorter landing run for a given set of conditions.

(c) Better aircraft control during braking.

(d) Reduced tendency for tyre blow-out.

7.2 Purpose

The purpose of the anti-skid system as fitted to aircraft wheel brakes is to prevent the wheels from skidding on wet or icy surfaces and to ensure that optimum braking effect can be obtained under all conditions, by modulating the hydraulic pressure to the brakes. Anti-skid units sense the rate of change of wheel deceleration, decreasing the hydraulic pressure applied to the brakes when a high rate of increase in deceleration exists consistent with an impending skid, and restoring it as the wheel accelerates again. A modulator valve, a form of hydraulic restrictor, is often fitted in conjunction with the anti-skid unit, to restrict the flow of fluid to the brake unit after initial brake application and to conserve main system pressure. This action tends to smooth out the brake operation.

There are two basic types of anti-skid systems in use, they are:

(a) Mechanical System.

(b) Electronic System.

7.3 Mechanical Anti-Skid System

In the mechanical anti-skid system the anti-skid unit is mounted either on the brake unit torque plate or within the axle bore. The anti-skid device is located within the hydraulic wheel brake system between the brake control valve and the brake unit, usually just prior to the brake unit. The anti-skid unit consists of a valve assembly connected to a flywheel which is driven by the associated aircraft wheel.

7.4 Mechanical Anti-Skid System Operation

During normal braking action, when no skid is present, the flywheel rotates at the same speed as the drive and the valve is closed allowing hydraulic fluid through the unit to the brake unit. This fluid is supplied from the brake control valve and is at maximum pressure for the control valve selection made. On leaving the anti-skid unit the fluid is directed to the inlet of the brake unit and then to the brake unit operating cylinders.

When the rotational speed of the aircraft wheel decreases rapidly, as when the aircraft wheel is about to skid, the inertia of the flywheel causes the anti-skid unit valve mechanism to operate opening the valve and reducing the hydraulic pressure in the brake unit. The anti-skid unit directs the fluid back to return. The reduced pressure which has also reduced the braking effect, allows the aircraft wheel to accelerate, the flywheel returns to its normal position causing the valve to close and the brake to be applied again, until the wheel is about to skid and the action is repeated. If the wheel bounces clear of the ground after brakes have been applied, the adjustment of the anti-skid unit allows the brake to be completely released for a period of time to prevent the wheel locking prior to making contact with the ground. Without this action a blow-out may occur.

Fig.7-1 shows the location of the anti-skid unit within the hydraulic system.

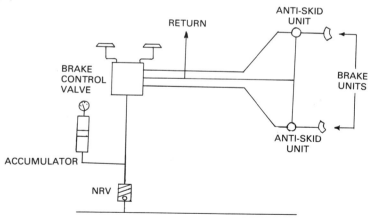

Fig.7-1. Anti-Skid Unit Location.

7.5 Installation of Mechanical Anti-Skid Unit

The mounting details of the various types of anti-skid unit vary considerably. However, to give a general example Fig.7-2 shows a typical mechanical anti-skid unit. This type would normally be mounted on the brake unit torque plate and the rubber tyre of the anti-skid unit drive wheel is so adjusted to be in contact with the inner rim of the aircraft's wheel. The unit is adjusted to produce a positive contact of the tyre with the wheel rim to produce a flat of half-an-inch to one inch to ensure no slippage of the anti-skid unit tyre occurs. Some anti-skid units are automatically adjusted whilst other types have to be manually adjusted by use of shims. Shims are thin pieces of metal which are inserted between the base of the anti-skid unit and the torque plate to achieve the correct adjustment.

Fig.7-2 shows an example of a mechanical anti-skid unit.

RETURN

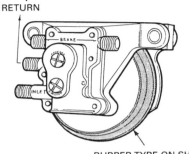

RUBBER TYRE ON SHELL DRIVEN
BY WHEEL RIM

Fig.7-2. Mechanical Anti-Skid Unit.

7.6 Electronic Anti-Skid Unit

The system comprises a wheel speed transducer, a control unit and an anti-skid valve in the brake pressure line, together with associated switches and check-out and warning lamps. The wheel speed unit may supply either d.c. or a.c. depending on the type of system used. Operation is basically similar to the mechanical system but the use of sophisticated logic circuits in the later types of electronic control units enables much finer control to be exercised. Further refinements such as strut oscillation damping circuits, touch-down protection and locked wheel protection, may also be incorporated and some systems automatically de-activate at low speed to prevent interference with normal taxying manoeuvres.

The method by which the wheel speed signal is processed in the control unit varies from type to type, but all operate on the basis that if any brake produces more torque than can be supported by the friction between the tyre and ground for the existing wheel load, the resulting impending skid will produce a smaller rotational velocity signal from the affected wheel. This reduced signal is detected by the anti-skid control circuits, which send a signal to the anti-skid control valve, causing brake pressure to be reduced sufficiently to correct the skid condition. Brake pressure will be re-applied to a level just below that which caused the skid and will then increase at a controlled rate. Control units normally contain circuits which provide warning of failure in the system and a self-test facility which enables the serviceability of the various components to be checked. Controls for the operation and testing of the anti-skid system are contained in the control unit and in the flight compartment.

TEST YOURSELF 7
BRAKE UNIT ANTI-SKID SYSTEMS

1. The use of an anti-skid unit will:
   (a) increase tyre wear.
   (b) increase the tendency of tyre blow-out.
   (c) increase maximum hydraulic pressure at the brake unit.
   (d) give better aircraft control during braking.

   Ref. 7.1.

2. The anti-skid unit is located within the wheel brake hydraulic system between:
   (a) the accumulator and the brake control valve.
   (b) the brake control valve and the brake unit.
   (c) the servo system and the brake control valve.
   (d) the brake unit and the aircraft wheel.

   Ref. 7.3.

3. A modulator valve is sometimes fitted between:
   (a) the anti-skid unit and the brake unit.
   (b) the brake unit and the aircraft wheel.
   (c) the brake control valve and the anti-skid unit.
   (d) the accumulator and the brake control valve.

   Ref. 7.2.

4. A modulator valve is a form of:
   (a) non-return valve.
   (b) one-way restrictor valve.
   (c) restrictor valve.
   (d) pressure relief valve.

   Ref. 7.2.

5. The mechanical anti-skid unit is normally driven by:
   (a) the aircraft wheel rim.
   (b) an electric motor.
   (c) the aircraft tyre.
   (d) a hydraulic motor.

   Ref. 7.5.

6. When an aircraft wheel is about to skid:
    (a) the hydraulic pressure is reduced at the brake unit.
    (b) the hydraulic pressure is reduced by the brake control valve.
    (c) the anti-skid unit valve closes.
    (d) the modulator valve closes.

    Ref. 7.4.

7. Use of anti-skid systems will tend to:
    (a) reduce the landing run.
    (b) reduce the landing speed.
    (c) increase the hydraulic force in the brake unit.
    (d) increase total hydraulic flow rate to the brake unit.

    Ref. 7.1.

8. The mechanical anti-skid unit is normally mounted on:
    (a) the aircraft wheel.
    (b) the undercarriage leg.
    (c) the brake rotor.
    (d) the brake torque plate.

    Ref. 7.5.

9. The action of the modulator valve tends to:
    (a) make brake operation smooth.
    (b) relieve excess pressure at the brake unit.
    (c) prevent brake pressure at the brake unit falling below a set value.
    (d) maintain a constant accumulator fluid pressure.

    Ref. 7.2.

10. Some anti-skid units are adjusted for wheel contact by shims; shims are:
    (a) an automatic adjusting system.
    (b) thin pieces of metal used for adjustment.
    (c) wear indicators.
    (d) tracks that fit on the wheel rim.

    Ref. 7.5.

8

SHOCK ABSORBERS

8.1 Introduction

The design of aircraft shock absorbers vary considerably, however their basic function is the same regardless of design details. First the shock absorber unit, which is normally part of the undercarriage unit assembly, must be capable of sustaining long periods in a static condition, that is when the aircraft is supported when parked on the ground. This condition is known as the static load condition.

Secondly the shock absorber must be capable of absorbing the impact of landing and sustaining the related drag and side loads. This is generally considered to be the landing load condition.

Thirdly during the compression of the shock absorber in the landing load condition considerable forces are applied generating very high pressures. Unless controlled, such pressures will generate a recoil action which will tend to force the aircraft back into the air. To prevent this occurring some form of recoil control must be fitted in the shock absorber.

8.2 Shock Absorber Types

There are generally three types of shock absorber fitted to modern aircraft, they are:

(a) The Oleo Pneumatic Type (without Separator)
Oleo pneumatic simply means the use of oil and air to perform the functions of the shock absorber. Air to basically absorb the compression loads, or landing loads, and oil to control the rate of recoil. Without Separator simply means the oil and air are not separated, that is they are in the same cylinder together.

(b) The Oleo Pneumatic Type (with Separator)
In this type the oil and air perform the same basic functions but are separated by a piston, much the same as the oil and air are separated in an accumulator. This is usually done on shock absorbers where the pressures generated tend to be high and therefore could case dieseling, or the spontaneous combustion of the oil and air.

(c) The Oil Compression Strut, or Liquid Spring
This type eliminates the use of air and uses oil only.

8.3 Oleo Pneumatic Shock Absorber (without Separator)

When the shock absorber is compressed, such as on landing, the air is compressed, absorbing the compression load. At the same time the oil is displaced and allowed to flow through a restrictor valve, or recoil control valve, opening the valve and allowing a rapid transfer of fluid. As the impact, or compression load has been absorbed, the shock absorber will start to extend, i.e. recoil. The recoil action is dampened by the restrictor valve closing allowing a slow transfer of fluid back through the valve assembly.

An example is shown in Fig.8-1.

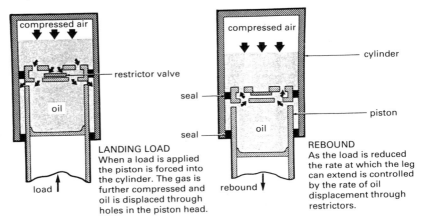

LANDING LOAD
When a load is applied the piston is forced into the cylinder. The gas is further compressed and oil is displaced through holes in the piston head.

REBOUND
As the load is reduced the rate at which the leg can extend is controlled by the rate of oil displacement through restrictors.

Fig.8-1. Oleo Pneumatic Shock Absorber (without Separator).

8.4 Oleo Pneumatic Shock Absorber (with Separator)

This type of shock absorber functions in the same way as the type without separator. It should be noted that to reduce the tendency of dieseling, modern oleo pneumatic shock absorbers use nitrogen instead of compressed air.

Fig.8-2 shows an example of the oleo pneumatic shock absorber with separator.

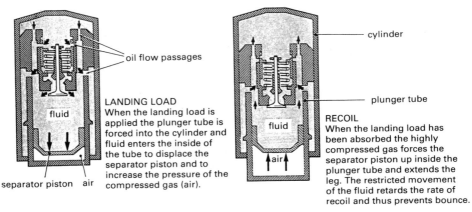

LANDING LOAD
When the landing load is applied the plunger tube is forced into the cylinder and fluid enters the inside of the tube to displace the separator piston and to increase the pressure of the compressed gas (air).

RECOIL
When the landing load has been absorbed the highly compressed gas forces the separator piston up inside the plunger tube and extends the leg. The restricted movement of the fluid retards the rate of recoil and thus prevents bounce.

Fig.8-2. Oleo Pneumatic Shock Absorber (with Separator).

8.5 Oil Compression Strut

This type of shock absorber is often used on nose, or tail undercarriage units as it tends to be smaller or more compact than the oleo pneumatic types.

As its name implies, this shock absorber type is filled with oil and operates without the cushioning effect of air. Because it does not use a compressed gas, either compressed air or nitrogen, the liquid spring is more compact and shorter in movement than the oleo pneumatic shock absorber. Both shock absorption and recoil movement are regulated by controlling the fluid movement from one side of a piston head to the other. Free flow in compression is facilitated and in recoil is restricted to dampen the rate of extension.

On the compression stroke pressure is generated within the cylinder by the piston rod being forced into the cylinder therefore reducing the volumetric capacity of the cylinder. This action causes the fluid to be compressed, generating a force which opposes the compression load.

An example oil compression shock absorber is shown in Fig.8-3.

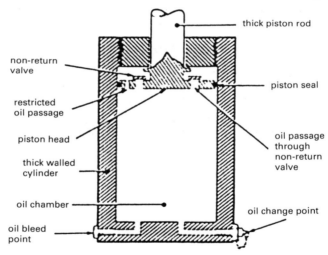

Fig.8-3. Oil Compression Shock Absorber (Liquid Spring).

8.6 Load/Extension Graph

It is essential that the shock absorber pressure is at the correct value prior to flight. To establish the pressure is correct for the load applied there are two basic types of graph which may be consulted.

(a) Load Extension Graph

The extension of the shock absorber is firstly measured at specific points as stated in the aircraft manual. The length for a given load is shown on the load extension graph. The shock absorber extension is proportional to the load applied.

An example of the measurement point and graph are shown in Fig.8-4.

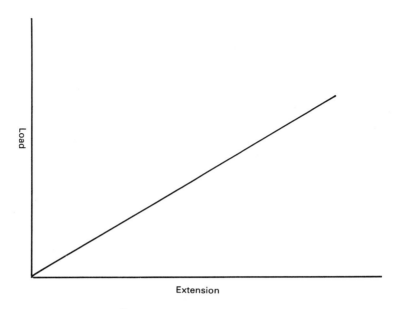

Fig.8-4. Load Extension Graph.

(b) Pressure Extension Graph

This graph is mostly used by the engineer which provides the correct extension measurement for a given shock absorber pressure.

When using this graph the physical pressure in the shock absorber must be checked. Fig.8-5 shows an example pressure extension graph.

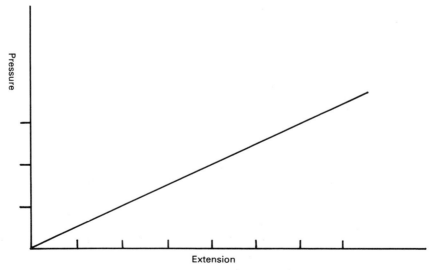

Fig.8-5. Pressure Extension Graph.

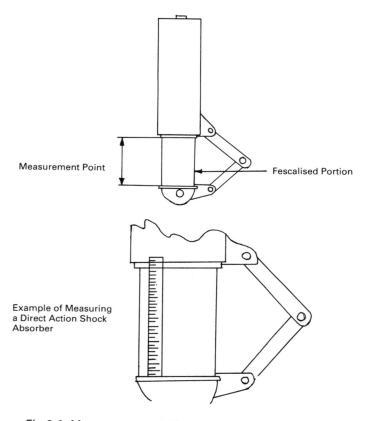

Measurement Point

Fescalised Portion

Example of Measuring
a Direct Action Shock
Absorber

Fig.8-6. Measurement of Shock Absorber Extension.

8.7 Extension of Shock Absorber Measurement

The points at which the shock absorber extension measurement is taken varies with design. Examples are shown in Fig.8-7 on an articulated undercarriage and a direct action unit.

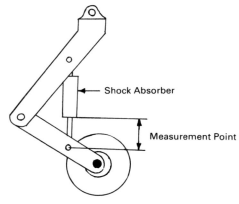

Shock Absorber

Measurement Point

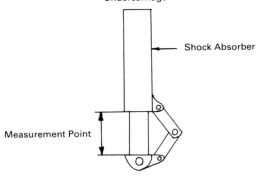

Fig.8-7. Direct Action Undercarriage.

TEST YOURSELF 8
SHOCK ABSORBERS

1. In an oleo pneumatic shock absorber the compression load is absorbed by:
   (a) the oil.
   (b) the air.
   (c) the compression spring.
   (d) the tension spring.

   Ref. 8.2.

2. The purpose of the separator piston in an oleo pneumatic shock absorber is to:
   (a) reduce pressure.
   (b) reduce the tendency of dieseling.
   (c) prevent overpressurisation.
   (d) separate the air and nitrogen.

   Ref. 8.2.

3. Recoil is controlled in an oleo pneumatic shock absorber by:
   (a) restricting oil flow.
   (b) restricting air flow.
   (c) restricting air and oil flow.
   (d) none of the above answers.

   Ref. 8.3.

4. The correct shock absorber pressure should be checked under static load conditions using:
   (a) a load extension graph.
   (b) a pressure extension graph.
   (c) a static pressure graph.
   (d) a compression graph.

   Ref. 8.6.

5. A Liquid Spring Shock Absorber is:
   (a) an oleo pneumatic shock absorber with separator.
   (b) an oleo pneumatic shock absorber without separator.
   (c) an oil compression strut.
   (d) an oil compression strut with separator.

   Ref. 8.2.

9

SUMMARY OF PRE-FLIGHT CHECKS

9.1 Introduction

Individual aircraft types require specific checks to be carried out prior to flight. The following are the general checks that should be carried out and some of the particular points that should be observed.

9.2 The General Structure

Included in the general structure are:

(a) Side Load Struts

(b) Drag Struts or Drag Links

(c) Attachment points of the Undercarriage, Drag Strut Attachments and Side Load Attachment points.

All of the above areas should be checked for any signs of:

(a) Damage in the form of dents, scratches and corrosion. Corrosion on aluminium alloy components will be indicated as a light grey powder on the surface of the metal. Corrosion on steel items will be shown as a reddish brown powder on the surface of the metal.

(b) Incorrect locking. Ensure that all items are locked correctly which include wire locking, split pins, stiff nuts, locking plates and tab washers. Fig.9-1a and b shows some examples of correct locking.

The student should note that questions on correct locking are currently being asked on a number of topics.

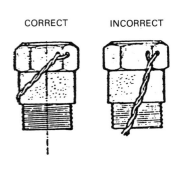

CORRECT   INCORRECT

ANGLE OF APPROACH

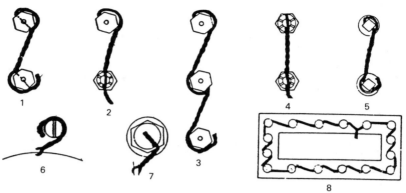

SAFETY WIRING METHODS

Fig.9-1a. Wire Locking.

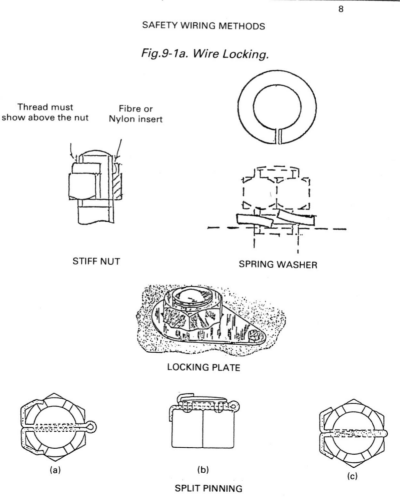

Fig.9-1b. Locking Nuts and Plates.

9.3 Tyre Inspection

Caution – When checking the tyres of an aircraft that has recently landed or completed a prolonged taxy and the brake units and tyres are still HOT, approach with caution. Remember it can take in excess of thirty minutes for the tyres and brakes to cool to normal ambient temperature. During this period in particular a tyre should be approached as if a 'Blow-out' is likely to occur.

The tyres should be examined for:

(a) Contamination
Contamination such as oil contamination which will discolour the rubber and cause swelling. This can ultimately lead to the separation of the rubber from the cords or plies.

(b) Wear
Examine the tyre for wear generally, paying particular attention to the wear indicator grooves. On a normal wear indicator groove to within two millimetres of the bottom of the groove. Where marker tie bars are used wear must not exceed a depth of wear to the top of the marker tie bars. On twin contact tyres the limit of wear is when the centre rubber first shows signs of being in contact with the ground.

(c) Reinforced Tread
Fabric which is moulded into the rubber tread to increase its resistance to wear must not be confused with plies when the tread becomes worn. The reinforcing fabric as it becomes exposed will hang as loose pieces from the tread, do not attempt to pull these loose ends of fabric.

(d) Pressure
Check the tyre pressures taking into account the temperature of the tyre.

(e) Creep Marks
On tubed tyres check that the creep of the tyre has not exceeded the width of the creep marks.

If a tubeless tyre has crept it is not a serious problem unless there are signs of damage to the bead area of the tyre, or if the tyre has started to deflate or is under pressure.

(f) Embedded Objects
The tyre should be examined for any stones or sharp objects which have been trapped within the tread grooves and any found should be removed before the next flight. Should such objects be left in the tread they may, through use, cause damage to the cords of the tyre.

Remember – Although the engineer is responsible for the serviceability of the aircraft it is also the pilot's responsibility that his aircraft is serviceable and ready for flight.

9.4 Wheel Inspection

The wheel should be examined for any signs of damage and in particular discolouration and any indication of cracking. The wheel may become discoloured in the form of the paint finish being turned to a very light brown or yellow colour which may indicate it has been subjected to excessively high temperatures. Cracking will usually take the form of hair line cracks should they occur. As the wheels and undercarriage are subjected to water, dirt etc on the runway, corrosion may be a problem.

9.5 Shock Absorbers

The shock absorbers should be checked for any signs of damage, corrosion, leakage and their correct extensions.

Leakage will normally be indicated by oil seeping from the shock absorber past filler point seals and may be shown leaking out past the main seals and collecting on the 'Fescalised', or sliding portion of the unit. Fescalising is a surface finish that is very hard wearing and is applied to sliding members. In appearance it is similar to chromium plating.

The correct extension of a shock absorber is of vital importance and should be checked against the appropriate graph. A further important point to note is, should the shock absorbers be of unequal extension the loading of the aircraft should be checked. Unequal shock absorber extensions may be due to an unbalanced fuel load. See Fig.9-2.

9.6 Heat and Stress Paint

Some parts of an aircraft may be painted with special paint, often green in colour, which changes colour if subjected to high temperatures or excessive stress; normally it changes from green to a purple or violet colour. Some undercarriage assemblies may employ the use of such paint.

9.7 Brake Units

The brake units should be examined for any sign of damage, their state of wear by checking the wear indicators and any signs of hydraulic fluid leakage at the brake inlet points and the pipelines leading to the brake units.

9.8 Anti-Skid Units

Where the mechanical type anti-skid unit is employed a check must be made of the anti-skid unit tyre contact. A check must also be made to ensure there is no hydraulic leakage at the various ports.

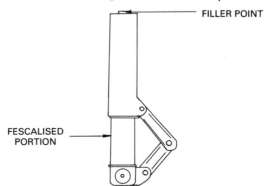

Fig.9-2. Shock Absorber Possible Leakage Points.

TEST YOURSELF 9
SUMMARY OF PRE-FLIGHT CHECKS

1. When checking the pressure of a tyre:
    (a) the tyre temperature must be taken into account.
    (b) the tyre must be in a no load condition.
    (c) the tyre must be under full load conditions.
    (d) the tyre must be set at the minimum pressure.

    Ref. 9.3.

2. A tubed tyre may be allowed to creep:
    (a) under no circumstances.
    (b) a maximum of the width of the creep marks.
    (c) a maximum of half the width of the creep marks.
    (d) a maximum of twice the width of the creep marks.

    Ref. 9.3.

3. The fescalised portion of a shock absorber is:
    (a) the sliding portion.
    (b) the static portion.
    (c) the attachment points.
    (d) another name for the drag strut.

    Ref. 9.5.

4. Heat indicator paint is applied to some components to:
    (a) give additional protection against high temperatures.
    (b) change colour when subjected to excessive temperatures.
    (c) prevent corrosion due to high temperatures.
    (d) indicate surface corrosion.

    Ref. 9.6.

5. Unequal extensions of undercarriage units may be due to:
    (a) temperature.
    (b) longitudinal C of G position.
    (c) low tyre pressures.
    (d) unequal fuel distribution.

    Ref. 9.5.

TEST YOURSELF
FINAL PRACTICE QUESTIONS

1. Drag loads imposed on an undercarriage unit on landing are absorbed by:
   (a) the torque links.
   (b) the shock absorber only.
   (c) the side load strut.
   (d) the drag strut.

   Ref. 1.2.

2. The shock absorber of an undercarriage unit is designed to:
   (a) absorb compression loads and dampen recoil.
   (b) absorb compression and drag loads.
   (c) absorb drag and side loads.
   (d) absorb compression, side and drag loads.

   Ref. 1.5.

3. To prevent the inner cylinder of the shock absorber from rotating within the outer cylinder:
   (a) drag links are fitted.
   (b) torsion bars are fitted.
   (c) anti-shimmy tyres are fitted.
   (d) torque links are fitted.

   Ref. 1.5.

4. When the undercarriage is up and locked up the position indicators will show:
   (a) three green lights.
   (b) three red lights.
   (c) all lights out.
   (d) three 'UP'.

   Ref. 1.7.

5. In order to spread the weight of the aircraft over a greater area to reduce wheel loading, modern aircraft employ:
   (a) multi-wheel units.
   (b) large balloon tyres.
   (c) tracked undercarriages.
   (d) undercarriage trim.

   Ref. 1.6.

6. A primary advantage of a nose-wheel tricycle undercarriage layout is:
   (a) better aerodynamic braking on landing.
   (b) elimination of nose-over during heavy braking.
   (c) retraction of a nose-wheel is generally easier.
   (d) heavy braking increases the wheel loading of the main under-carriage.

   Ref. 2.3.

7. Take-off with a tail-wheeled undercarriage:
   (a) provides better lift without additional drag penalties.
   (b) provides lift during early take-off run with drag penalties.
   (c) provides increased stability.
   (d) eliminates tail swing.

   Ref. 2.3.

8. During heavy braking the loading on the main wheels of a tail-wheeled undercarriage layout:
   (a) are greater than a nose-wheel layout.
   (b) are essentially the same as a nose-wheel layout.
   (c) are less than a nose-wheel layout.
   (d) are none of the above answers.

   Ref. 2.3.

9. A major disadvantage of a tail-wheeled aircraft after landing and during taxying is:
   (a) no use of brakes in case of nose-over.
   (b) poor forward vision by the pilot.
   (c) a reduction in aerodynamic drag.
   (d) loss of rudder control.

   Ref. 2.3.

10. An advantage of a tandem undercarriage layout is:
    (a) the elimination of undercarriage units from the wing.
    (b) reduces the take-off run.
    (c) increases lateral stability during the take-off run.
    (d) a lower unstick speed.

    Ref. 2.5.

11. Bogie undercarriages are used on modern aircraft to:
    (a) increase the wheel loading.
    (b) reduce the landing run.
    (c) reduce the take-off run.
    (d) reduce the wheel loading.
                                            Ref. 2.7.

12. Bogie trim is the term used to describe:
    (a) the folding of the undercarriage unit during retraction.
    (b) the steering of the undercarriage during landing.
    (c) the trimming of the undercarriage to reduce shimmy.
    (d) the action of nose-wheel steering.
                                            Ref. 2.9.

13. Bogie trim:
    (a) requires manual operation by the pilot.
    (b) is an automatic function when the undercarriage is selected.
    (c) is an emergency operation.
    (d) must be activated by the pilot prior to undercarriage selection.
                                            Ref. 2.9.

14. Bogie trail:
    (a) ensures all wheels spin-up on touch-down simultaneously.
    (b) prevents individual wheels rotating at a higher r.p.m.
    (c) provides a progressive spin-up of the wheels on touch-down.
    (d) ensures the wheels spin-up prior to touch-down.
                                            Ref. 2.10.

15. On modern aircraft it is mandatory:
    (a) that all aircraft tyres be electrically conducting.
    (b) that only the nose or tail-wheel tyre be electrically conducting.
    (c) that tyres must be fully insulating.
    (d) that tyres on main landing gear be electrically conducting.
                                            Ref. 5.12.

16. Modern aircraft tyres are normally inflated with:
    (a) hydrogen to reduce weight.
    (b) nitrogen to reduce the risk of fire.
    (c) air only.
    (d) nitrogen to reduce leakage rate.
                                            Ref. 5.2.

17. In a tubeless tyre assembly air or nitrogen is retained by:
    (a) an inner tube.
    (b) the casing plies.
    (c) an inner rubber liner.
    (d) an outer rubber liner.

Ref. 5.5.

18. The rate of wear of an aircraft high speed tyre is reduced by:
    (a) a cord reinforced tread.
    (b) a higher tyre pressure.
    (c) a reduced tyre pressure.
    (d) a breaker strip.

Ref. 5.4.

19. A major advantage of a tubeless tyre is:
    (a) lower tyre pressures may be used.
    (b) a considerable saving in weight.
    (c) less tyre wear.
    (d) easier to make the wheel airtight.

Ref. 5.6.

20. The region of a tyre in which the tread is located is known as the:
    (a) shoulder.
    (b) wall.
    (c) bead.
    (d) crown.

Ref. 5.7.

21. The most widely used type of tread pattern is the:
    (a) chined.
    (b) block.
    (c) ribbed.
    (d) plain.

Ref. 5.8.

22. A chined tyre is used to:
    (a) reduce tyre wear.
    (b) deflect water.
    (c) indicate tyre wear.
    (d) dissipate heat.

Ref. 5.9.

23. A method employed as an anti-shimmy device is the:
    (a) ribbed tyre.
    (b) chined tyre.
    (c) block tyre.
    (d) twin contact tyre.

Ref. 5.9.

24. The term ply rating means the:
    (a) number of plies per inch.
    (b) number of plies per centimetre.
    (c) strength of a tyre.
    (d) maximum speed at which it may be operated.

Ref. 5.14.

25. The rotors of a piston rod adjustment type brake unit are manu-factured from:
    (a) steel.
    (b) copper.
    (c) stainless steel.
    (d) solid chromium.

Ref. 3.8.

26. A set of brake plates as fitted to a piston rod adjuster type brake unit consist of:
    (a) two outer plates.
    (b) the total number of plates fitted.
    (c) two plates of the same dimensions.
    (d) one inner and one outer plate.

Ref. 3.8.

27. Caliper brake units:
    (a) are mostly used on large aircraft.
    (b) are only used on large aircraft.
    (c) are only used on helicopters.
    (d) are used on light aircraft and helicopters.

Ref. 3.10.

28. Caliper brake units are normally fitted with:
    (a) a single disc or plate.
    (b) two plates or discs.
    (c) four plates.
    (d) three plates.

Ref. 3.10.

29. Caliper plates or discs are driven by:
    (a) axle drive blocks.
    (b) rubber drive wheels.
    (c) the tyre bead.
    (d) wheel drive blocks.

    Ref. 3.10.

30. The operating cylinders of a segmented plate type brake unit are mounted in:
    (a) the axle assembly.
    (b) the stator.
    (c) the rotor.
    (d) the torque plate.

    Ref. 3.14.

31. On most segmented plate type brake units the working clearance is maintained by:
    (a) adjustment of the piston rod.
    (b) automatic brake clearance adjuster.
    (c) adjustment by the engineer after each landing.
    (d) adjustment by the wear indicator.

    Ref. 3.15.

32. On a segmented type rotor assembly:
    (a) each segment has a tenon.
    (b) each segment has two tenons.
    (c) each alternate segment has a tenon.
    (d) each segment has a drive block.

    Ref. 3.16.

33. Segmented type plate brake segments are manufactured from:
    (a) steel.
    (b) stainless steel.
    (c) copper.
    (d) chromium.

    Ref. 3.16.

34. Brake plates are segmented to:
    (a) reduce warping.
    (b) increase surface area.
    (c) reduce surface area.
    (d) reduce operating temperature.

    Ref. 3.16.

35. The tenons of a modern brake unit are driven by:
    (a) drive blocks mounted on the wheel.
    (b) drive blocks mounted on the tyre.
    (c) drive blocks mounted on the drive ring.
    (d) drive blocks on the wheel axle.

    Ref. 3.3.

36. The stator on a segmented type brake unit is:
    (a) driven by the wheel drive blocks.
    (b) driven by the axle.
    (c) mounted on the axle.
    (d) mounted on the torque plate.

    Ref. 3.12.

37. The self adjusters are mounted on:
    (a) the axle.
    (b) the torque plate.
    (c) the thrust ring.
    (d) the wear indicators.

    Ref. 3.14.

38. On a segmented type plate brake unit the working clearance is established after each brake application by:
    (a) the wear indicators.
    (b) centrifugal force.
    (c) the return springs.
    (d) the piston rod adjuster.

    Ref. 3.15.

39. By segmenting the rotors of modern brake units:
    (a) lower operating temperatures are achieved.
    (b) less wear takes place.
    (c) a saving of weight is achieved.
    (d) smoother braking is achieved.

    Ref. 3.16.

40. Aircraft wheels are normally manufactured from:
    (a) steel.
    (b) magnesium alloy only.
    (c) aluminium alloy only.
    (d) aluminium or magnesium alloy.

    Ref. 4.1.

41. On a wheel designed to take a tubed tyre to assist in preventing tyre creep:
    (a) a knurled flange is incorporated.
    (b) creep marks are fitted.
    (c) tubeless tyres are fitted.
    (d) over-inflation is used.

    Ref. 4.2.

42. The bead seat of a wheel is tapered to:
    (a) reduce weight.
    (b) increase strength.
    (c) hold the tyre on the wheel.
    (d) prevent tyre creep.

    Ref. 4.2.

43. Fusible alloy plugs are fitted to:
    (a) all wheels.
    (b) nose and tail wheels only.
    (c) tubed and tubeless assemblies.
    (d) tubeless assemblies.

    Ref. 4.5.

44. A fusible alloy plug is designed to:
    (a) operate at excessive pressure.
    (b) operate at excessive temperature.
    (c) operate on selection by the pilot.
    (d) operate on selection by the engineer.

    Ref. 4.5.

45. A green fusible alloy plug has an operating temperature of:
    (a) 155 degrees C.
    (b) 177 degrees C.
    (c) 199 degrees C.
    (d) 277 degrees C.

    Ref. 4.5.

46. A fusible alloy plug is designed to:
    (a) release the tyre pressure rapidly.
    (b) release the tyre pressure only when selected by the pilot.
    (c) release the tyre pressure slowly.
    (d) reduce the tyre pressure if the pressure is excessive.

    Ref. 4.5.

47. Tyre creep on a wheel designed to use a tubeless tyre is minimised by:
    (a) a knurled flange.
    (b) rubber tyre blocks.
    (c) a tapered bead seat.
    (d) rubber adhesive.

    Ref. 4.3.

48. Air is prevented from leaking through the wheel of a tubeless tyre assembly by:
    (a) a resin coating.
    (b) a rubber sleeve.
    (c) a rubber tube.
    (d) a rubber liner.

    Ref. 4.3.

49. The type of bearings most commonly used on aircraft wheels are:
    (a) ball and or roller bearings.
    (b) needle roller bearings.
    (c) plain bearings.
    (d) knurled bearings.

    Ref. 4.4.

50. A tyre moulded with marker tie bars in the ribbed grooves is worn to its limits when:
    (a) it is worn to the bottom of the tie bar.
    (b) it is worn to the top of the marker tie bar.
    (c) the marker tie bar changes colour.
    (d) it is worn to the base of the groove in which the tie bar is moulded.

    Ref. 5.20.

51. A Marstrand Tyre is worn to its limits when:
    (a) the centre of the crown shows signs of being in contact with the ground.
    (b) the twin contacts are worn to their base.
    (c) the twin contacts are worn to their indicator lines.
    (d) the colour of the contact rubber changes.

    Ref. 5.20.

52. Under-inflation of a tyre may lead to:
    (a) excessive vibration.
    (b) prolonged tyre life.
    (c) tyre creep.
    (d) cooler running.

    Ref. 5.21.

53. The rated pressure of a tyre is the pressure when:
    (a) the tyre is under maximum load.
    (b) the tyre is cold and under no load.
    (c) the tyre is cold and under maximum load.
    (d) the tyre is warm and under normal working load.

    Ref. 5.21.

54. The pressure to which a tyre should be inflated when under load is:
    (a) the rated pressure.
    (b) the rated pressure plus 4 per cent.
    (c) the rated pressure minus 4 per cent.
    (d) the rated pressure plus 10 per cent.

    Ref. 5.21.

55. It is mandatory to fit electrically conducting tyres:
    (a) to all aircraft wheels.
    (b) to all aircraft main wheels.
    (c) to all aircraft wheels fitted with brake units.
    (d) to the nose or tail wheel.

    Ref. 5.22.

56. Wear indication on reinforced treaded tyres is normally provided by:
    (a) a wear indicator groove.
    (b) multi-wear indicator grooves.
    (c) colour code bars.
    (d) marker tie bars.

    Ref. 5.20.

57. The maximum creep permitted on a tubed tyre is:
    (a) half the width of the creep mark.
    (b) the width of the creep mark.
    (c) twice the width of the creep mark.
    (d) no visible movement indicated.

    Ref. 5.19.

58. A grey dot on the wall of a tyre indicates:
    (a) the light spot.
    (b) the heavy spot.
    (c) an awl vent.
    (d) a creep mark.

    Ref. 5.16.

59. A high speed tyre is one which is designed to be used:
    (a) at a maximum speed up to 160 mph.
    (b) at a maximum speed up to 100 mph.
    (c) at speeds over 160 mph.
    (d) at a maximum speed of up to 110 mph.

    Ref. 5.15.

60. An anti-skid unit is normally fitted in the wheel brake hydraulic system:
    (a) just prior to the brake control valve.
    (b) between the accumulator and the brake control valve.
    (c) between the brake control valve and the brake unit.
    (d) between the brake unit and the wheel.

    Ref. 7.2.

61. The modulator valve is fitted in the anti-skid system between:
    (a) supply pressure and brake control valve.
    (b) accumulator and brake control valve.
    (c) the brake control valve and anti-skid unit.
    (d) the anti-skid unit and brake unit.

    Ref. 7.1.

62. The modulator valve:
    (a) boosts system fluid pressure.
    (b) restricts fluid flow to the brake unit after initial application of brakes.
    (c) restricts fluid flow to the brake units at initial brake application.
    (d) reduces hydraulic supply system pressure.

    Ref. 7.1.

63. When an aircraft wheel has a tendency to skid when fitted with an anti-skid system:
    (a) brake pressure is reduced by the anti-skid unit.
    (b) brake pressure is reduced by the brake control valve.
    (c) brake pressure remains constant at the brake unit.
    (d) brake pressure will be reduced by the accumulator.

    Ref. 7.1.

64. A mechanical type anti-skid unit is driven by:
    (a) the wheel rim.
    (b) drive blocks.
    (c) tenons.
    (d) the aircraft tyre.

    Ref. 7.2.

65. In order to increase the braking force when applying wheel brakes:
    (a) increased foot pedal pressure is applied.
    (b) a separate pressure lever is operated.
    (c) accumulator pressure is increased.
    (d) supply pressure must be increased.

    Ref. 6.1.

66. Operation of the brake control valve is achieved by:
    (a) mechanical operation only.
    (b) accumulator pressure.
    (c) system pressure.
    (d) servo pressure.

    Ref. 6.5.

67. Initial operation of the brake units is achieved with the use of:
    (a) servo pressure.
    (b) system pressure.
    (c) mechanical pressure.
    (d) accumulator pressure.

    Ref. 6.3.

68. Emergency operation of the wheel brakes is normally achieved with the use of:
    (a) system pressure.
    (b) servo pressure.
    (c) mechanical operation.
    (d) accumulator pressure.

    Ref. 6.3.

69. When brakes are released the return fluid goes back to:
    (a) the reservoir via the control valve.
    (b) the reservoir from the operating cylinders.
    (c) the accumulator via the control valve.
    (d) the reservoir via the main system supply.

    Ref. 6.5.

70. Hydraulic supply for the operation of the wheel brake system is provided by:
    (a) the accumulator only.
    (b) the main system accumulator only.
    (c) the main supply system.
    (d) the servo system.

    Ref. 6.2.

71. In an oleo pneumatic shock absorber most of the compression load is absorbed by:
    (a) the restrictor valve.
    (b) the oil.
    (c) the air.
    (d) the transfer holes.

    Ref. 8.2.

72. Dieseling in an oleo pneumatic shock absorber may be prevented by:
    (a) the use of hydrogen instead of air.
    (b) the use of nitrogen instead of air.
    (c) the use of oil only.
    (d) the use of air only.

    Ref. 8.2.

73. A liquid spring shock absorber employs the use of:
    (a) air only.
    (b) air and oil.
    (c) oil only.
    (d) nitrogen only.

    Ref. 8.2.

74. Another name given to the liquid spring shock absorber is:
    (a) the oil compression strut.
    (b) the oleo pneumatic shock absorber.
    (c) the oleo shock absorber.
    (d) the oil strut.

                                                    Ref. 8.2.

75. The recoil action of an oleo pneumatic shock absorber is dampened by:
    (a) the air passing through the restrictor.
    (b) the restrictor valve closing.
    (c) the restrictor valve opening.
    (d) the coil spring.

                                                    Ref. 8.3.

76. Pressure is generated in a liquid spring shock absorber by:
    (a) the piston rod reducing the volumetric capacity of the cylinder.
    (b) the piston rod increasing the volumetric capacity of the cylinder.
    (c) the separator piston.
    (d) the movement of the restrictor valve.

                                                    Ref. 8.5.

77. As the liquid spring shock absorber does not use gas to absorb the compression loads:
    (a) it tends to be longer than other shock absorber types.
    (b) it is only used on light aircraft.
    (c) it tends to be more compact.
    (d) it tends to have a greater volumetric capacity than other types.

                                                    Ref. 8.5.

78. The pressure in an aircraft shock absorber under static load conditions is checked with the use of:
    (a) a load extension graph.
    (b) a deflection gauge.
    (c) a static load chart.
    (d) none of the above.

                                                    Ref. 8.6.

79. When an aircraft is stationary on the ground the shock absorber is under:
    (a) landed load conditions.
    (b) compression load conditions.
    (c) static load conditions.
    (d) extended load conditions.

    Ref. 8.1.

80. A tyre fitted with ribbed wear indicator grooves is worn to its limits when it is worn to:
    (a) within 2mm of the top of the groove.
    (b) within 2mm of the bottom of the groove.
    (c) within 5mm of the top of the groove.
    (d) within 5mm of the bottom of the groove.

    Ref. 9.3.

81. As tread reinforcing fabric becomes exposed through tyre wear:
    (a) loose pieces should be removed.
    (b) the tyre is unserviceable.
    (c) this should be ignored.
    (d) the tread should be trimmed back.

    Ref. 9.3.

82. A tubeless tyre is:
    (a) allowed to creep the width of the creep marks.
    (b) not allowed to creep at all.
    (c) allowed to creep half the width of the creep marks.
    (d) allowed to creep providing no damage occurs to the tyre bead.

    Ref. 9.3.

83. A twin contact tyre is worn to its limits when:
    (a) the centre section of tyre is in contact with the ground.
    (b) the marker tie bars start to wear.
    (c) it is worn to within 2mm of the base of the indicator groove.
    (d) it is worn to within 5mm of the base of the indicator groove.

    Ref. 9.3.

84. Oil contamination of a tyre:
    (a) can be ignored.
    (b) may cause the rubber to swell.
    (c) should be cleaned off with water.
    (d) should be reported to the engineer after the flight.

    Ref. 9.3.

85. Corrosion on an aluminium alloy undercarriage component will be indicated by:
    (a) a reddish brown deposit.
    (b) a green powder on the surface.
    (c) a light grey powder on the surface.
    (d) a black powder on the surface.

    Ref. 9.2.

86. On some light aircraft the inner cylinder of the shock absorber is prevented from rotating within the outer cylinder by:
    (a) rubber dampers.
    (b) spring loading.
    (c) splines.
    (d) drag struts.

    Ref. 1.5.

87. Three undercarriage green lights indicate:
    (a) the undercarriage is down.
    (b) the undercarriage is selected down.
    (c) the undercarriage is down and locked down.
    (d) the undercarriage is up and selected down.

    Ref. 1.7.

88. The tenons of a brake plate are driven by:
    (a) the drive blocks in the wheel.
    (b) the tenons in the wheel.
    (c) the axle hub.
    (d) the aircraft tyre.

    Ref. 3.8.

89. The stator assembly of a modern brake unit:
    (a) rotates with the aircraft wheel.
    (b) is driven by the drive blocks.
    (c) carries the friction pads.
    (d) is bolted to the aircraft wheel.

    Ref. 3.17.

90. A caliper brake unit:
    (a) is normally fitted with one disc only.
    (b) is used in conjunction with a drum brake.
    (c) is used on any type of aircraft.
    (d) is always mechanically operated.

    Ref. 3.10.

IT IS ESSENTIAL TO KNOW THE
ANSWERS TO THE FOLLOWING QUESTIONS

1. Three red undercarriage position indicator lights indicate:
   (a) the undercarriage is unlocked.
   (b) the undercarriage is selected down.
   (c) the undercarriage is locked up.
   (d) the undercarriage is selected down.

Ref. 1.7.

2. The purpose of torque links is to:
   (a) limit the range of movement of the shock absorber.
   (b) prevent the shock absorber inner cylinder rotating within the outer cylinder.
   (c) absorb compression loads.
   (d) absorb drag loads.

Ref. 1.5.

3. On modern aircraft it is mandatory that:
   (a) all tyres are electrically conducting.
   (b) only main wheel tyres are electrically conducting.
   (c) tail- or nose-wheel tyres are electrically conducting.
   (d) only wheels with brake units are electrically conducting.

Ref. 5.12.

4. The term Ply Rating means:
   (a) the number of plies per mm.
   (b) the number of plies per cm.
   (c) the number of plies per inch.
   (d) the strength of the tyre.

Ref. 5.14.

5. Brake plates are segmented to:
   (a) prevent warping.
   (b) increase stability.
   (c) increase surface area.
   (d) reduce operating temperature.

Ref. 3.16.

6. Fusible alloy plugs are fitted to:
   (a) all main wheels.
   (b) all aircraft wheels.
   (c) tubeless tyre wheels only.
   (d) tubeless tyre wheels with brake units only.

   Ref. 4.5.

7. A fusible alloy plug is fitted to relieve the gas in the tyre due to:
   (a) excessive temperature.
   (b) excessive pressure.
   (c) a blow-out.
   (d) a heavy landing.

   Ref. 4.5.

8. A red fusible alloy plug is designed to function at:
   (a) 155 degrees C.
   (b) 155 psi.
   (c) 199 degrees C.
   (d) 199 psi.

   Ref. 4.5.

9. A tyre must be changed when it is worn to:
   (a) the base of the marker tie bar.
   (b) the top of the marker tie bar.
   (c) within 2mm of the marker tie bar.
   (d) the base of the wear indicator groove.

   Ref. 5.20.

10. Twin contact tyres are worn to their limits when:
    (a) the centre rubber is in contact with the ground.
    (b) the wear is within two mm of the base of the groove.
    (c) the marker tie bar is exposed.
    (d) the contact rubber is worn to within 2mm of the centre rubber.

    Ref. 5.20.